Raintree Steck-Vaughn

Illustrated SCIENCE ENCYCLOPEDIA

Volume
5

CLO – DAG

RSVP

**RAINTREE
STECK-VAUGHN**
P U B L I S H E R S
The Steck-Vaughn Company

Austin, Texas

Published by Raintree Steck-Vaughn Publishers, an imprint of
Steck-Vaughn Company.

Executive Editor	Diane Sharpe
Senior Editor	Anne Souby
Design Manager	Joyce Spicer

This edition edited and designed by Andromeda Oxford Ltd.

Andromeda Editorial and Design

Project Manager	Julia Roles
Editorial Manager	Jenny Fry
Design	TT Designs, T&S Truscott
Cover Design	John Barker

Library of Congress Cataloging-in-Publication Data
Raintree Steck-Vaughn illustrated science encyclopedia.
         p.   cm.
     Includes bibliographical references and index.
     Summary: A twenty-four volume set containing brief articles
on science topics.
     ISBN 0-8172-3943-X (set)
     ISBN 0-8172-3923-5 (Volume 5)
     1. Science—Encyclopedias, Juvenile.   [1. Science—
Encyclopedias.]   I. Raintree Steck-Vaughn Publishers.
Q121.R354   1997
503—dc20   96-11078
                                           CIP
                                            AC

Printed and Bound in the United States of America.
1 2 3 4 5 6 7 8 9 10 IP 00 99 98 97 96

USING THE RAINTREE STECK-VAUGHN ILLUSTRATED SCIENCE ENCYCLOPEDIA

You are living in a world in which science, technology, and nature are very important. You see something about science almost every day. It might be on television, in the newspaper, in a book at school, or some other place. Often, you want more information about what you see.

The *Raintree Steck-Vaughn Illustrated Science Encyclopedia* will help you find what you want to know. It contains information on many science subjects. You may want to find out about computers, the environment, space exploration, biology, agriculture, or mathematics, for example. They are all in the *Raintree Steck-Vaughn Illustrated Science Encyclopedia*. There are many, many other subjects covered as well.

There are twenty-four volumes in the encyclopedia. The articles, which are called entries, are in alphabetical order through the first twenty-two volumes. On the spine of each volume, below the volume number, are some letters. The letters above the line are the first three letters of the first entry in that volume. The letters below the line are the first three letters of the last entry in that volume. In Volume 1, for example, you see that the first entry begins with **AAR** and that the last entry begins with **ANT**. Using the letters makes it easy to find the volume you need.

In Volume 23, there are three special features—reference charts and tables, a bibliography, and an index. In Volume 24, there are interesting projects that you can do on your own. The projects are fun to do, and they help you discover and understand important science principles. Many can give you ideas that can help you develop your own science fair projects.

Main Entries There are two kinds of main entries in the *Raintree Steck-Vaughn Illustrated Science Encyclopedia*. Many of the entries are major topics that are spread over several pages. The titles of these entries are shown at the top of the page in a yellow box. Other entries required less space to cover the topic fully. The titles of these main entries are printed in capital letters. They look like this: **ABALONE**. At the beginning of some entries, you will see a phonetic pronunciation of the entry title, such as (ăb′ ə lō′ nē).

In the front of each volume, there is a pronunciation key. Use it the same way you use your dictionary's pronunciation key.

Cross-References Within the main entries are cross-references referring to other entries in the encyclopedia. Within an entry, they look like this: (see MAMMAL). At the end of an entry, they look like this: *See also* HYENA. These cross-references tell you where to find other helpful information on the subject you are reading about.

Projects At the end of some entries, you will see this symbol: ⚡ PROJECT 1. It tells you which projects related to that entry are in Volume 24.

Illustrations There are thousands of photographs, drawings, graphs, diagrams, tables, and other illustrations in the *Raintree Steck-Vaughn Illustrated Science Encyclopedia*. They will help you better understand the entries you read. Captions describe the illustrations. Many of the illustrations also have labels that point out important parts.

Activities Some main entries include activities presented in a special box. These activities are short projects that give you a chance to work with science on your own.

Index In Volume 23, the index lists every main entry by volume and page number. Many subjects that are not main entries are also listed in the index, as well as the illustrations, projects, activities, and reference charts and tables.

Bibliography In Volume 23, there is also a bibliography for students. The books in this list are on a variety of topics and can supplement what you have learned in the *Raintree Steck-Vaughn Illustrated Science Encyclopedia*.

The *Raintree Steck-Vaughn Illustrated Science Encyclopedia* was designed especially for you, the student. It is a source of knowledge for the world of science, technology, and nature. Enjoy it!

PRONUNCIATION KEY

Each symbol has the same sound as the darker letters in the sample words.

ə	balloon, ago	îr	deer, pier	r	root, tire
ă	map, have	j	join, germ	s	so, press
ā	day, made	k	king, ask	sh	shoot, machine
âr	care, bear	l	let, cool	t	to, stand
ä	father, car	m	man, same	th	thin, death
b	ball, rib	n	no, turn	*th*	then, this
ch	choose, nature	ng	bring, long	ŭ	up, cut
d	did, add	ŏ	odd, pot	ûr	urge, hurt
ě	bell, get	ō	cone, know	v	view, give
ē	sweet, easy	ô	all, saw	w	wood, glowing
f	fan, soft	oi	boy, boil	y	yes, year
g	good, big	ou	now, loud	z	zero, raise
h	hurt, ahead	ŏŏ	good, took	zh	leisure, vision
ĭ	rip, ill	ōō	boot, noon	'	strong accent
ī	side, sky	p	part, scrap	ˏ	weak accent

GUIDE TO MEASUREMENT ABBREVIATIONS

All measurements in the *Raintree Steck-Vaughn Illustrated Science Encyclopedia* are given in both the customary system and the metric system [in brackets like these]. Following are the abbreviations used for various units of measure.

Customary Units of Measure

mi. = miles	cu. yd. = cubic yards
m.p.h. = miles per hour	cu. ft. = cubic feet
yd. = yards	cu. in. = cubic inches
ft. = feet	gal. = gallons
in. = inches	pt. = pints
sq. mi. = square miles	qt. = quarts
sq. yd. = square yards	lb. = pounds
sq. ft. = square feet	oz. = ounces
sq. in. = square inches	fl. oz. = fluid ounces
cu. mi. = cubic miles	°F = degrees Fahrenheit

Metric Units of Measure

km = kilometers	cu. km = cubic kilometers
kph = kilometers per hour	cu. m = cubic meters
m = meters	cu. cm = cubic centimeters
cm = centimeters	ml = milliliters
mm = millimeters	kg = kilograms
sq. km = square kilometers	g = grams
sq. m = square meters	mg = milligrams
sq. cm = square centimeters	°C = degrees Celsius

For information on how to convert customary measurements to metric measurements, see the Metric Conversions table in Volume 23.

CLOCK AND WATCH

A clock is an instrument that shows the time. A watch is a small, portable clock. A clock or watch often has a dial, or face, on which there is a ring of evenly spaced numbers from 1 to 12. The hands on the face of the clock or watch may point toward any of the numbers, thereby showing the time. Many clocks and watches display a changing number, in digits, instead of having moving hands and stationary numbers. These are called digital clocks and watches.

History Sundials, invented more than four thousand years ago, are the oldest known instruments designed to show the time. The sun, as it moves across the sky, casts a shadow on the dial. A sundial tells time by measuring the length or the angle of the shadow.

Other devices that were once used to tell time include candle clocks, water clocks, and hourglasses. With candle clocks, time was measured by the rate of a burning candle. The water clock was a leaking bowl. The hours were noted as the water surface dropped past lines marked inside the bowl. Su Song, a Chinese scholar, created a very large mechanical water clock in the eleventh century. In the hourglass, sand flowed from one part of a container into

POCKET WATCH

By the mid-1700s, the mechanisms of pocket watches had been perfected to keep very accurate time. This watch was made around 1890.

another part at a steady rate. By measuring the amount of sand in either container, a person could tell how much time had passed.

Historians believe the first mechanical clocks were made by a number of inventors during the late 1200s. These clocks, working by a system of

CLOCK TOWER

The first clocks in public places were housed in the towers of churches and monasteries to tell people when it was time to come and pray. These clocks had no faces or hands, but they signaled the time by striking bells. Tower clocks, like this one in Milwaukee, Wisconsin, are still popular today.

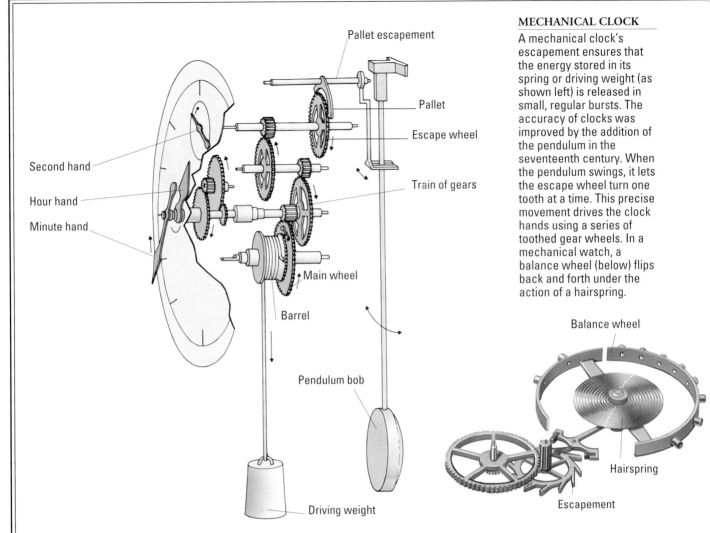

Pallet escapement

Pallet

Escape wheel

Train of gears

Second hand

Hour hand

Minute hand

Main wheel

Barrel

Pendulum bob

Driving weight

MECHANICAL CLOCK

A mechanical clock's escapement ensures that the energy stored in its spring or driving weight (as shown left) is released in small, regular bursts. The accuracy of clocks was improved by the addition of the pendulum in the seventeenth century. When the pendulum swings, it lets the escape wheel turn one tooth at a time. This precise movement drives the clock hands using a series of toothed gear wheels. In a mechanical watch, a balance wheel (below) flips back and forth under the action of a hairspring.

Balance wheel

Hairspring

Escapement

weights, had no hands or pendulum, which is a body that hangs from a fixed point and is free to swing (see PENDULUM). Instead, these clocks had a bell that rang to mark the hour.

The word *clock* probably comes from the French word *cloche* or the German word *Glocke,* both of which mean "bell." The dial and hour hand had been added by the middle 1300s. The first clocks that worked by a system of springs are thought to have been developed in the late 1400s.

During the 1600s, Christian Huygens, a Dutch scientist, worked out the conditions for perfect oscillation (back-and-forth movement) of a pendulum. A balance wheel and balance spring were invented in the 1670s, widely replacing the pendulum. In an instrument with a balance wheel and balance spring, one end of the spring is fixed. The other end follows the backward and forward motion of the balance wheel. The spring winds and unwinds as the wheel swings. The

manufacture of smaller clocks and watches started around the middle 1600s. Early watches had only an hour hand and were made in unusual shapes, including skulls and crosses. By the late 1600s, some watches had a minute hand. These watches, commonly called pocket watches, were the most popular watch style for more than 200 years.

By the start of the 1700s, minute hands became common. By the middle of the century, inventors had developed most of the devices that are part of modern mechanical clocks.

Wristwatches, at first designed only for women, became common in the late 1800s. They grew in popularity for men during World War I (1914–1918).

The second hand on clocks and watches became common in the 1900s. Electric clocks were common by the 1920s. Quartz-based clocks appeared by the 1930s. The first atomic clock was invented in the 1940s. Electric dial watches were introduced in the 1950s. Digital clocks and watches became popular in the 1970s.

Types of clocks in use today Modern clocks range from small, plain models to huge, decorative works of art. Whether dial or digital, every clock has two main parts: (1) the case and (2) the movement, also called the works, inside the case. In addition to showing time, the movement supplies power to run the clock. The movement also keeps time. Timekeeping in most clocks is based on the frequency (rate) of some repeated action, such as the action of a pendulum or spring device as mentioned earlier. Atomic clocks are based on the vibrations of cesium atoms. Atomic clocks are the most accurate clocks ever made. They are accurate to within millionths of a second per year.

The two main types of clocks are mechanical clocks and electric clocks. Mechanical clocks are powered by various devices that must be wound.

Some mechanical clocks have to be wound every day. Some do not have to be wound for a week or more. Almost all mechanical clocks are dial clocks. Some are weight driven. Others are spring driven.

Weight-driven clocks are powered by a weight that hangs from a chain or cord. When the clock is wound, the chain or cord gets wrapped around a drum. The weight is drawn up near the drum. Gravity pulls the weight down. As the weight lowers, the cord or chain slowly unwinds, turning the drum. The drum then turns a number of gear wheels. These wheels are connected in a series called a train. Each of these wheels turns at a specific speed. Certain wheels are attached to the hands of the clock. A pendulum and a device called the escapement work together to control the weight from being lowered too fast. The escapement is made up of an escape wheel and a verge. The escape wheel is connected to the train and turns when the clock runs. The pendulum, the timekeeping device of the clock, swings from side to side at a steady

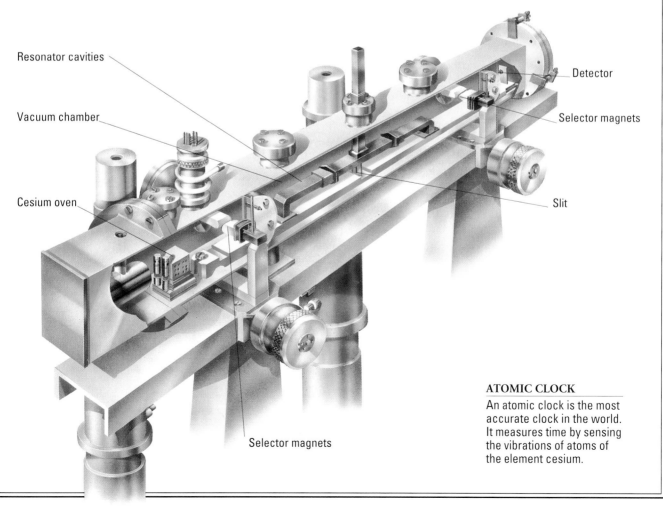

Resonator cavities

Vacuum chamber

Cesium oven

Detector

Selector magnets

Slit

Selector magnets

ATOMIC CLOCK

An atomic clock is the most accurate clock in the world. It measures time by sensing the vibrations of atoms of the element cesium.

rate. As it swings, it tilts the verge from side to side. With each tilt, two hooks called pallets catch the escape wheel and stop it. When the pendulum swings back, the pallets release the wheel, and the wheel turns slightly. This process regulates the wheels in the train. It also causes the *tick-tock* sound.

In spring-driven clocks, the mainspring gets wound up when the clock is wound. The mainspring unwinds slowly. This motion turns the wheels in the train. Some spring-driven clocks have a battery that rewinds the main spring automatically. The escapement in a spring-driven clock is similar to the escapement in a weight-driven clock. However, many spring-driven clocks have a balance wheel instead of a pendulum. A coiled spring known as the balance spring, or hairspring, is connected to the balance wheel. This spring coils and uncoils. Such action makes the balance wheel swing at a steady rate.

The second main group of clocks, electric clocks, can be battery powered or line powered. Some battery-powered clocks have a balance wheel or a pendulum that controls their speed. Others have a tuning fork or a tiny bar of quartz crystal. Receiving power from the battery, a tuning fork or crystal vibrates at high, steady frequencies. Quartz-based clocks contain an electric circuit (see CIRCUIT, ELECTRIC). This circuit changes the number of vibrations into time information. Most of these quartz clocks are accurate to within sixty seconds a year.

A line-powered clock gets its power from an electric outlet. The current from the outlet also regulates the clock's speed. The flow of alternating current changes its direction 120 times per second (see ALTERNATING CURRENT). In most cases, a motor in the clock counts the changes in direction, using this information to control the time. Most digital clocks are line powered. In some digital clocks, the digits are printed on moving tapes or on flip cards. Others have a liquid crystal display (LCD). This type uses digits that reflect the light around it. A light-emitting diode (LED) display has digits shaped from electronic devices called diodes, which give off light (see LCD; LED).

Types of watches in use today Most modern watches are wristwatches, but pocket watches are still used. Other watches are mounted in pins, rings, or necklaces. Watches, like clocks, vary greatly from inexpensive plain models to decorative models costing thousands of dollars. The two main groups of watches are dial and digital, based on how they show the time. The two kinds of dial watches are mechanical watches and electric watches. Mechanical watches, powered by a mainspring, work in the same way as mechanical clocks. Electric watches get their power from a tiny battery.

Digital watches are quartz based and have no moving parts. The circuits in a digital watch change the time information directly into an electric digital display on the watch face. As in digital clocks, digital watches have two main kinds of electric displays, the LCD or the LED. Diodes use more power than the LCDs. To save power, LED watches show the time only when the person turns on the display.

OLD AND NEW CLOCKS
A traditional alarm clock (above) is a spring-driven clock. Slowly rotating hands indicate the time. A digital clock (below) is powered by electricity. The time is indicated by numbers (digits) that change every minute.

CLONE A clone is an organism asexually produced from and genetically identical to another organism. *Clone* can also refer to a group of such organisms (see ASEXUAL REPRODUCTION; GENE; REPRODUCTION). Except for a rare mutation, clones are also exactly alike in appearance (see MUTATION). A colony of bacteria is a clone because each of the millions of bacteria has descended from a single bacterium by a splitting process called mitosis (see MITOSIS).

Simple organisms such as algae and fungi can reproduce asexually and produce a clone. Plants can produce clones by vegetative propagation (see VEGETATIVE PROPAGATION). Strawberries, for example, send out specialized stems called stolons, each of which produces new plants.

Some animals, such as sponges and hydra, can reproduce asexually or undergo regeneration to produce a clone (see REGENERATION). Frogs and salamanders have been artificially cloned by destroying the nucleus of an egg and replacing it with the nucleus of any body cell from another organism of the same species. The egg develops into an adult with all the characteristics of the donor.

Cloning has a variety of uses in medical practice. For example, in the mid-1970s, a technique was developed for transferring genes from one organism to another. This involves combining DNA from a plant or animal cell with the DNA in bacteria. When the bacterium divides, its clones contain the plant or animal DNA in addition to its original DNA. This type of cloning has been used to produce the cells that produce growth hormone, insulin, and interferon. Growth hormone and insulin are used to treat disorders of the endocrine system. Interferon is a protein that fights the reproduction of viruses (see DNA; ENDOCRINE; HORMONE; INTERFERON).

Recently, clones have been made of the genes of the AIDS virus. By studying the functions of the cloned genes, scientists can learn more about how the virus works. Scientists are also researching ways to combine cancer cells with immune cells. The idea is that cloned cells will produce antibodies, which will prevent further spread of the cancer (see AIDS; ANTIBODY; IMMUNITY). It may soon be possible to clone organs and tissues. Some attempts have also been made to produce a human being by cloning. The attempts were based on the fact that because DNA contains an organism's entire genetic code, it may be possible to "grow" a new organism from one of its DNA molecules. In 1993, scientists succeeded in splitting a human embryo to produce two identical embryos, a process sometimes known as cloning. If embryos like these were successfully implanted in a woman's uterus, they could develop into identical twins. This is possible because cells in very young embryos, unlike other cells, are unspecialized. This means that any one of them could develop into a complete organism. As an embryo matures, its cells develop into many different kinds of cells, such as muscle, nerve, or skin cells, each specialized to perform a specific function. Once a cell is specialized, it cannot become any other kind of cell. In order to clone a human being from a specialized cell, scientists would probably have to find a way to change the cell into another type of cell, such as an unspecialized cell. No such technique has yet been developed. Therefore, most scientists feel that producing a human clone from cells other than embryo cells is far beyond current knowledge and technology. Also, the idea of cloning humans is surrounded by controversy for ethical reasons.

CLOUD A cloud is a mass of water droplets or ice crystals that floats in the air. Water gets into the air

CLOUD

This view of the earth from space shows cloud formations over the Eastern Hemisphere.

from evaporation of oceans, lakes, and rivers (see EVAPORATION). As height above the earth increases, temperature drops. Cooler air cannot hold as much water vapor as warm air. When the temperature drops below the dew point, some of the water vapor condenses into water droplets, forming clouds (see CONDENSATION; DEW POINT). The water droplets may remain liquid below the freezing point, 32°F [0°C]. If this occurs, they are called supercooled (see SUPERCOOLING). In clouds high up in the atmosphere, where the temperature is far lower, the water droplets become ice crystals. Rain and snow fall from clouds of supercooled water droplets and ice crystals.

There are two major cloud types. Cumuliform clouds are puffy white clouds. They have a flat bottom and are often very tall. When cumuliform clouds grow very tall and dark, they are called cumulonimbus clouds, or thunderheads. The other important cloud type is stratiform clouds. Stratiform clouds are long blanket clouds that form in layers. They often bring rain or snow. Ten important cloud types within the three major types are listed in the table.

See also ATMOSPHERE.

 PROJECT 25

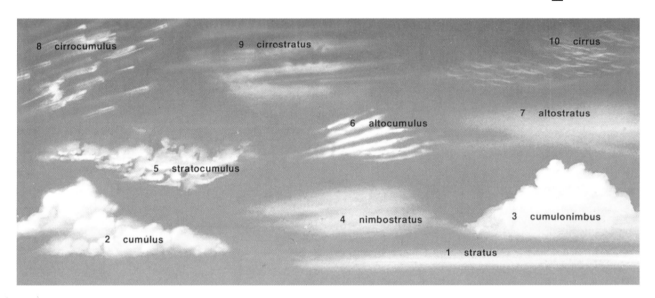

CLASSIFICATION OF CLOUDS			
Height (figures refer to middle latitudes)	**Type of Cloud**	**Symbol**	**Description**
Low Clouds Up to 8,000 ft. [2,439 m]	Stratus Cumulus Cumulonimbus Nimbostratus Stratocumulus	St Cu Cb Ns Sc	Uniform, gray cloud layer. May cover high ground. Detached heaps of cloud, considerable vertical development. Brilliant white when lit by the sun. Fairly horizontal base, but bulging upper parts. The thundercloud. Dense, with the upper portion often flattened. Its base may be very dark. Gray, often dark, layer of cloud, sometimes blurred by falling rain or snow. Grayish white sheet of cloud, with definite shading. Composed of rounded masses that sometimes merge.
Medium Clouds 8,000-15,000 ft. [2,439–4,573 m]	Altocumulus Altostratus	Ac As	Grayish white sheet or patch of cloud, with definite shading. Composed of rounded masses, often merged. Grayish sheet of cloud, either fibrous or uniform in appearance.
High Clouds Above 15,000 ft. [4,573 m]	Cirrocumulus Cirrostratus Cirrus	Cc Cs Ci	Thin sheet or patch of cloud in the form of ripples or rounded small masses, often merged. Transparent film of fibrous, whitish cloud. It is often the cause of the "halo" seen around the sun or moon, which it produces by the effect of light on ice crystals. Delicate white, detached clouds with fibrous appearance. Its many forms include "mares' tails."

CLOVE The clove is a tropical, evergreen tree that produces flower buds that are dried and used as a spice. The tree grows as tall as 40 ft. [12 m] and has large, pointed leaves. The flowers are purple and grow in clusters. If the flower bud is picked and dried before it blooms, it can be used to make a powder or an oil with a strong odor and a sharp taste. Clove powder and oil of cloves are used as a flavoring for cakes and candies. Oil of cloves is also used as a dental anesthetic. Whole clove buds are used to flavor hams and other foods.
See also EVERGREEN.

Flower buds

Dried buds

CLOVE

The clove tree belongs to the same family as the eucalyptus tree, both of which contain strong-smelling oils. The clove tree is a native of Indonesia, but it is now grown in several other parts of the world. The island of Pemba, off the coast of Tanzania in East Africa, produces most of the world's cloves today.

CLOVER Clover is the name given to more than three hundred species of herbaceous plants that belong to the pea family (see HERBACEOUS PLANT; PEA FAMILY). These plants grow wild in fields throughout temperate areas of the Northern Hemisphere and in southern Africa and South America. Clover is often cultivated as a food for livestock. Since clover is an excellent agent of nitrogen fixation, it is frequently plowed back into the ground to enrich the soil (see NITROGEN FIXATION).

Red clover is the most important variety of clover. Although it is a perennial (meaning that it lives for more than two years), it usually dies within three years. Red clover may grow as tall as 24 in. [60 cm] and can be pollinated only by a bumblebee (see POLLINATION). Other common types of clover are white clover, crimson clover, and strawberry clover.

Clover leaves usually have three leaflets attached. Four-leaf clovers, with four leaflets, have long been considered a sign of good luck by some people.

CLUB MOSS A club moss is any of more than 1,200 species of small evergreen plants growing in damp habitats nearly all over the world, including cold mountain slopes and tropical forests (see EVERGREEN). A member of the phylum Lycopodiophyta, the club moss is not a true moss. The club moss produces a horizontal stem called a rhizome on or just below the surface of the soil. Roots and upright green stems covered with small, needlelike or scalelike leaves grow from the rhizome. The green plant is the asexual or nonsexual stage of the life cycle (see ALTERNATION OF GENERATIONS). Small cones grow singly or in clusters at the tips of the stems and scatter tiny spores that grow into the sexual phase of the life cycle. This phase is a rarely seen underground sausage-shaped body on which the sex organs and sex cells are produced.

CLOVER
The flowerheads of clovers consist of many tiny flowers, each packed with nectar from which bees can make honey.

CLUB MOSS
Club mosses are related to ferns. This one grows in the Arctic and on the mountains of Canada and Europe.

During the Carboniferous period, which lasted from 345 million years ago to 280 million years ago, club mosses grew to heights of 100 ft. [30 m]. Their remains are an important part of coal.

See also MOSS, LIVERWORT, AND HORNWORT; PLANT KINGDOM.

CLUTCH A clutch is a device that is used to transmit power from an engine to a drive shaft. The clutch makes it possible to keep an engine running even though the drive shaft has stopped turning. This is more efficient than stopping the engine each time the shaft is stopped.

Clutches can be found on many familiar objects, including farm and factory machinery, clothes washers, dishwashers, sewing machines, power lawnmowers, and bicycles. The most familiar clutch, however, is the one used in automobiles. The driver of a car needs some device to disconnect the engine from the drive wheels in stop-and-go traffic and to shift gears. The clutch does this job. There are two types of automobile clutches, the mechanical clutch and the hydraulic clutch.

The mechanical clutch consists of one metal disk pressed tightly between two other disks. It is operated by a foot pedal controlled by the driver. The disk in the middle is called the clutch plate or driven plate. It is connected to a shaft leading into the transmission. The transmission contains sets of gears that allow the drive shaft to turn at various speeds. The other two disks in the mechanical clutch are the fly wheel, which is mounted on the engine crank shaft, and the pressure plate. The pressure plate is attached to the clutch shaft. When the driver takes his or her foot off the clutch pedal to engage the clutch, powerful springs push the pressure plate toward the flywheel. The pressure plate holds the clutch plate tightly against the flywheel. Friction between the clutch plate and the rotating flywheel causes the clutch plate to turn. The clutch shaft on which it is mounted rotates and transmits power to the transmission. When the driver pushes down on the clutch pedal to disengage the clutch, the pressure plate and clutch plate move away from the flywheel.

The hydraulic clutch is used on all cars that have automatic transmissions. This clutch automatically engages and disengages and thus eliminates the foot pedal. The hydraulic clutch is linked electrically to the gearshift lever and the engine. It operates automatically when the driver moves the gearshift lever to change gears, or when the engine requires gear changes because of the speed at which the car is moving. The hydraulic clutch is contained in a housing that looks like a large doughnut. Disks containing a series of fanlike blades are mounted inside the housing. The disk closest to the engine is connected to the engine crankshaft. When the crankshaft turns, this disk turns. Another disk is connected to a shaft leading into the transmission. The housing is filled with oil, called hydraulic fluid. When the driver moves the gearshift lever, the front disk begins to turn. Its blades are positioned so that they spin the oil toward the other disk. The second disk's blades are positioned so that the spinning oil, or fluid, forces the disk to turn in the same direction as the first disk. The driven disk, or the one nearest the transmission, can never turn quite as fast as the disk connected to the engine crankshaft because the fluid action has a bit of slack in it. That is why it is possible for a car with a hydraulic clutch to stand still while the engine is running slowly even though the transmission is in gear. The hydraulic clutch also smooths out jerks caused by the shifting of gears or sudden changes in speed.

See also AUTOMOBILE; HYDRAULICS.

CNIDARIA (nī dă′rē ə) Cnidaria is a phylum of the animal kingdom. The phylum is sometimes called Coelenterata. The sea anemone, coral, jellyfish, and hydra are members of Cnidaria. They range in size from microscopic to over 6.6 ft. [2 m] in diameter. There are about 10,000 different kinds.

The body of a cnidarian is a hollow sac. The animal brings in food and removes waste through the one opening in the body. The opening is usually surrounded by arms called tentacles. These tentacles capture food and bring it into the opening, where it is eaten. Cnidarians eat small invertebrates (animals without backbones) and fishes. The tentacles are clothed with stingers called nematocysts.

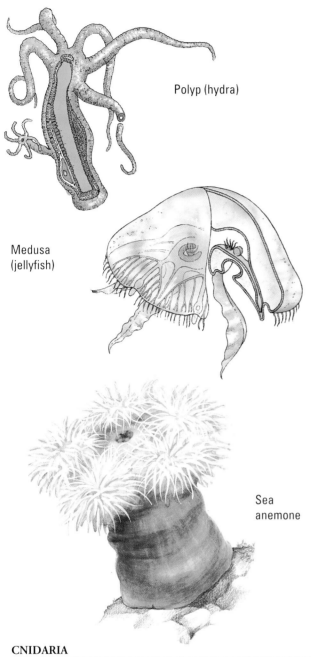

Polyp (hydra)

Medusa
(jellyfish)

Sea
anemone

CNIDARIA

The two main groups of the cnidarians are the polyps and the medusas (top and middle). Both animals pictured have been cut away to show the central cavity where food is digested. The plumose anemone (bottom) is a very common sea anemone. Up to 12 in. [30 cm] high, it has as many as 1,000 short tentacles in dense bunches.

The nematocysts look like little spears at the ends of slender threads. If a small animal touches the tentacles, the nematocysts shoot out and either spear or wrap around the prey. They often inject a poison that kills or paralyzes the animal. The nematocysts of such cnidarians as Portuguese men-of-war sting swimmers who brush against them (see PORTUGUESE MAN-OF-WAR).

Cnidarians can be divided into two main groups: medusas and polyps. Medusas are jellyfish, which swim freely about. Polyps are saclike animals that anchor their bodies to rocks, or the bottom of the sea or a lake, or underwater plants. Hydras and sea anemones are single polyps, and most corals are polyps that live together in colonies. Some cnidarians have both medusa and polyp stages in their life cycles. The medusas are produced from special polyp buds that, in time, break free and swim away. The medusas then produce eggs and sperm that unite and develop into polyps.

See also ALTERNATION OF GENERATIONS; REPRODUCTION.

COAL Coal is a naturally occurring accumulation of vegetable matter. It has been changed by heat and pressure over a long period of time into a lightweight, black to brown, rocklike material. Coal is a source of energy. It is also a source of raw materials for the chemical industry. The United States produces more coal than any other country. Forty percent of the world coal supply is located in North America.

Coal formation Large quantities of coal formed during a time called the Carboniferous period, which lasted from about 363 million years ago to about 290 million years ago. Parts of the earth were then covered by swamplike seas. Because of the hot, moist climate, gigantic plants were able to grow. When the plants died, they sank into the swamp, and new plants replaced them. As the newer plants died, layers of dead material began to form. Mud and sand settled on top of this layer and pressed some of the water out. Eventually the land rose, and more plants grew on the surface. These new plants died, decayed, and were covered by mud and sand again. This cycle continued for millions of years. Many layers of stratified matter formed as decaying material was forced further beneath the surface (see STRATIFICATION). Great pressure was produced by these many layers. The pressure, together with chemical reactions, gradually transformed the decayed material into coal. This is why coal is called a fossil fuel.

COAL—A fossil fuel
The black dusty nature of coal is a familiar sight in any traditional industrial area. Through a microscope it is often possible to detect the plant fibers and pollen grains that show its vegetable origin. Occasionally we can see the actual ferny leaves preserved in the layers.

Sometimes, the outline of an ancient plant can be seen in a lump of coal.

Kinds of coal Coal consists mainly of carbon, hydrogen, oxygen, and nitrogen. Coal has no chemical formula because the elements that compose it appear in different ratios. Coal is classified by geologists as sedimentary rock (see SEDIMENTARY ROCK). There are several different types of coal. Peat is a material in the first stages of coal formation. When removed from the ground, it may contain as much as 90 percent water. Peat must be dried out before use. Dry peat contains up to 60 percent carbon (see PEAT).

Lignite contains less water than peat. Lignite is a brown or black coal. When dried, brown lignite is 60 to 75 percent carbon. Black lignite is often called sub-bituminous coal and may be more than 80 percent carbon (see LIGNITE).

Bituminous coal is the most common type of coal, containing up to 80 percent carbon. It has many industrial uses as well as being an important fuel. Most of the bituminous coal mined in the United States comes from the area just west of the Appalachian Mountains.

Anthracite is the final product of the coal formation process. It contains very little water and is about 95 percent carbon. Most anthracite is mined in eastern Pennsylvania. Almost half of the anthracite produced is used for heating. It is the most expensive type of coal.

Coal mining Coal is usually mined in one of two ways, either strip (surface) mining or underground mining.

Strip mining is done by removing the soil above a coal deposit. When the coal is exposed, explosives are used to break it up. The coal is then loaded into trucks and taken away. Although strip mining is an efficient way of obtaining coal, it has a damaging effect on the environment.

Underground mining reaches coal deposits deep below the surface. In a shaft mine, a hole is dug straight down to the coal. Air for the miners is provided by ventilation shafts. Practically all of the coal is mined using machines and explosives. The coal removed from the deposit is loaded into a wagon-like car that carries it to the surface. The miners enter and leave the shaft by elevator.

Another method of underground mining is called slope mining. Slope mining is used to reach coal deposits in hillsides. A sloped tunnel leads from the outside to the coal deposit. Trains are used to move the coal, as well as to transport the miners in and out of the mine.
See also MINING.

COAL GAS Coal gas is a fuel made up mainly of hydrogen and methane. It is obtained when coal is heated in the absence of air. The coal is heated in large, airtight ovens called retorts. The lack of air prevents the coal from burning. When the temperature reaches 2,010°F [1,100°C], the coal gives off vapors and gases and changes to coke. These vapors and gases are treated to remove important by-products, such as tar, ammonia, and hydrogen sulfide. The coal gas that has also been produced is stored in large containers, called gas holders. It is burned to produce heat for factories and homes.
See also COKE.

COAST The coast is the land next to the sea. Waves are always changing the shape of the coast. In some places, the waves erode, or wear away, the coast. In other places, they deposit, or pile up, material to form new land (see EROSION).

The changing level of the sea has a great effect on the coast. Since the Ice Age, water from melted ice has made the oceans much deeper and has flooded many coasts. In some places, earth movements have caused the coastlines to emerge, or rise out of the water. For example, the east coast of the United States emerged from the sea and later partially submerged. A submerged coastline is one that has sunk into the sea. Submerged coasts often have long shallow inlets called rias, which are filled with water.

Coastal erosion Sand and pebbles along the shore are always moving and rubbing against each other with the movement of the waves. This motion grinds down the sand and pebbles to much smaller particles. During storms, large waves trap air in holes and cracks in the rock along the shoreline. When the air is released, it may have enough force to break apart the rock. Storm waves can also lift up pebbles and rocks and throw them against the shore. This may undercut cliffs to form caves. Soft rock erodes faster than hard rock. On coasts where

COAST

Coasts are either wearing away or building up. Where they are building up, we find beaches of smooth gravel or sand (top). Where they are wearing away, we find crumbling cliffs battered and broken by the beating of the waves (below).

there are both soft and hard rocks, the soft rock may erode completely, leaving the hard rock sticking out into the sea. This jutting-out area is called headland. When two caves meet in a headland, a natural arch is formed. If the arch falls, a pillar of rock called a stack remains.

Coastal deposition Some material that either erodes from coasts or is carried into the sea by rivers may be deposited elsewhere. It may form a beach or other new land area. However, in places where the water is moving in more than one direction, the eroded material builds up into long, narrow ridges called spits. Spits occur most often in bays at the mouth of a river. When a spit cuts a bay off from the ocean, it is called a baymouth bar. Tombolos are spits that link an island to the mainland or connect two islands. Spits and bars are common along the east coast of the United States and the east coast of England.

COBALT Cobalt (Co) is a silver white metallic element (see ELEMENT). George Brandt, a Swedish chemist, discovered cobalt in 1737.

Cobalt got its name from the German word *Kobold,* meaning "underground spirit." Cobalt is found mainly in Canada and Australia. The metal is usually found in compounds (substances containing two or more elements) with sulfur and arsenic.

Cobalt alloys (mixtures of metals) are used to make parts for jet engines and for cutting tools. Because cobalt has strong magnetic properties, its alloys are also used to make magnets. Many cobalt compounds are used as coloring matter, especially in ceramics. Cobalt-60 is a strongly radioactive isotope used in medicine for treating cancer (see RADIATION THERAPY; RADIOACTIVITY).

Cobalt's atomic number is 27. Its relative atomic mass is 58.94. Cobalt melts at 2,723°F [1,495°C] and boils at 5,612°F [3,100°C].

COBRA The cobra is a poisonous snake that belongs to the family Elapidae. There are several species in Africa and southern Asia, though the greater variety of cobras is found in Africa. All true cobras lay eggs instead of giving birth to live young.

Cobras are often called hooded snakes. When excited or disturbed, a cobra raises the front part of its body and spreads some of its ribs. This flattens the neck and makes it look as if the snake were wearing a hood.

The Indian cobra grows to about 6 ft. [1.8 m] in length and ranges in color from yellowish brown to dark brown. This cobra is sometimes called the spectacled cobra because the marks on the back of its hood look like a pair of eyeglasses.

COBRA

Cobras are the snakes most often used by snake charmers in Africa and southern Asia because they look quite spectacular when they rear up and spread their necks to form "hoods." They cannot hear the snake charmer's music because they have no ears. They may sway back and forth in time to the movements of the snake charmer and his pipe.

The spitting cobra of Africa sprays its venom (poison) in an outward, jetlike stream toward the eyes of its victim. The poison can be sprayed over a distance of 8 ft. [2.4 m] and can cause extreme irritation, blindness, or even death if the victim is not treated immediately.

The longest of all poisonous snakes, the king cobra, lives in southeastern Asia. It sometimes grows to a length of 18 ft. [5.5 m]. When it raises itself and spreads its hood, it is a spectacular sight. The king cobra is mostly olive green and is believed by some people to be trainable.

The king cobra feeds on other snakes, but rats and other rodents are the main food of the other cobras. They also eat fishes, birds, and frogs. The cobra's natural enemy is the mongoose.

See also MONGOOSE; SNAKE.

COCAINE Cocaine is a powerful mind-altering drug. In recent years, it has become popular with many drug abusers. Its widespread use has caused serious problems in many communities. Cocaine production and selling are linked with the rise of certain kinds of violent crimes. For example, "territorial wars"—fights over the areas that cocaine sellers believe they control—are common.

Cocaine is a white powder made from the leaves of the coca plant, a flowering shrub that grows throughout the Andes Mountains of South America (see COCA PLANT). Cocaine users generally inhale the powder through their noses. This is called "snorting." Repeated snorting can cause damage to the inside of the nose. Some users inject cocaine mixed with water into their bloodstream. Cocaine also can be changed chemically to produce a very powerful and addictive form, called "crack." Crack looks like small shavings of soap. Crack's effects on the human body and mind are like cocaine's effects, only more intense. Also, because users smoke or inject crack, the drug reaches the brain almost instantly. This smoking is called "freebasing" by users of crack. Crack became more widely used in the 1980s because of the intensity of its effects and because of its cheap price compared with that of ordinary cocaine.

For centuries, coca leaves were chewed by the Indians who lived at the higher elevations of Peru and Bolivia. Chewing the leaves made them feel less hungry and tired. The Incas, the Indians who ruled the west coast of South America before the coming of the Spaniards in the 1500s, believed the coca plant was divine. Their legends said that the plant was a special gift from the sun god's son. The right to own and use coca leaves was closely controlled by the Inca king.

In the 1800s, doctors began using cocaine, made from coca leaves, as an anesthetic (substance that causes loss of feeling), especially for eye surgeries. Today, however, cocaine has largely been replaced by other anesthetics. Nonmedical cocaine use became illegal in the United States when Congress passed the Harrison Narcotics Act in 1915. Drug abusers today buy cocaine illegally from drug dealers.

Cocaine and crack are powerful stimulants and take effect quickly. Almost at once, they cause a rise in the user's blood pressure, body temperature, and breathing and heart rates. Cocaine abusers often feel energetic. They have a false sense of intense happiness and well-being while using the drug. This period usually lasts about ten to thirty minutes. However, this "high" is quickly followed by a "down," or period of severe, prolonged depression. This depression is often as intense, or more so, than the high that went before it.

Cocaine and crack users often feel driven to take ever-increasing amounts of the drugs to feel the highs they produce and to try to avoid the downs that follow. The user becomes addicted. Sometimes, especially in the case of crack, the user can become addicted after the first time using the drug (see ADDICTION).

Some cocaine and crack users behave in unpredictable, violent, and paranoid ways. This behavior is called cocaine psychosis. It can occur in anybody who uses cocaine or crack. It appears to be most common, however, in those who use crack. People with cocaine psychosis become anxious and suspicious of others to the point that they feel their lives are in danger. It is not unusual for users to have hallucinations, during which they hear and see things that are not real.

Besides addiction and behavioral problems, cocaine and crack can cause other medical problems. They can produce convulsions, heart and respiratory failure, and death—even after a single dose. The risk of such problems increases as users increase the amount and frequency of drug use. In addition, users who share the hypodermic needles and syringes with which they inject cocaine risk catching serious diseases. These diseases include AIDS and the liver disease known as hepatitis (see AIDS; HEPATITIS). Cocaine users then run the risk of passing these diseases on to their sexual partners or to their unborn babies.

Cocaine and crack pose other dangers for pregnant women. These drugs can cause miscarriages, premature deliveries, and deliveries in which the baby is born dead. Babies who do live often have physical and emotional problems, making them sickly and bad tempered. Such "cocaine babies" also run increased risks of convulsions and sudden infant death syndrome (crib death). Nursing mothers also can pass cocaine to their babies through their milk.

Because the pure drug is so valuable, illegal dealers dilute, or "cut," cocaine with other, cheaper substances. These cutting substances increase the risk involved in cocaine use. The users do not know the purity of, or how much, cocaine they are taking into their bodies. Also, some of the cutting substances can cause side effects. These side effects include nervousness, abdominal cramps, body aches, diarrhea, and even death.

Because of the intense and long-lasting cravings that cocaine and crack produce, most users find it impossible to stop using these drugs without help. Treatment usually begins with detoxification. The user tries to stop using the drug and rid his or her body of it. Detoxification is followed by some combination of individual, group, and family therapy. The addict tries to understand the causes of his or her drug use and works to change to and live a drug-free life.

Information on cocaine abuse and treatment is available anywhere in the United States by looking in the Yellow Pages under Drug Abuse and Addiction Information and Treatment. There are many treatment centers and hotlines ready to help. *See also* DRUG; STIMULANT.

COCA PLANT The coca plant is one of a group of South American shrubs or small trees. It grows as tall as 6.6 ft. [2 m] and produces small leaves 1 to 3 in. [2.5 to 7.6 cm] long. Some Peruvian and Bolivian Indians chew the leaves to help fight hunger and fatigue. The leaves cause numbness of the lips and mouth when chewed because they contain several drugs, including cocaine. Cocaine also is extracted from the leaves and sold, mostly illegally to drug abusers (see COCAINE).

COCKATOO A cockatoo is a large bird that belongs to the parrot family. It is found in the forests of Australia, New Guinea, the Philippines, and nearby islands. Cockatoos are usually light colored, but a few are black. Long feathers form crests on their heads and the crests can be raised and lowered. Cockatoos often are kept as pets. *See also* PARROT.

COCKLE A cockle is a saltwater animal that belongs to the class Pelecypoda or Bivalvia of the Mollusca phylum. It is a bivalve (see BIVALVE). Its soft, fleshy body is enclosed by two hard shells that are hinged together to open like a book. There are many different species and they live in the sand on the bottom of the ocean, sometimes 3,200 ft. [1,000 m] below the sea surface. They are, however, most common in shallow coastal waters.

Cockles feed by straining little particles out of the water that they suck into their shells. Some species of cockles are eaten by people. *See also* MOLLUSCA.

COCKROACH The cockroach is any of more than 4,000 species of insects making up the suborder Blattidae of the order Dictyoptera. Cockroaches, often just called roaches, have flattened bodies covered with hard but flexible casings. Many are wingless, but others have four wings folded flat on the back. They have two hairlike antennae and long, strong legs covered with bristles (see ANTENNAE). Cockroaches vary in appearance, but the most common varieties are brown and 0.4 to 1.2 in. [1 to 3 cm] long.

Most cockroaches live outdoors under rocks or

COCKROACH
This Australian cockroach, shown with her egg capsule, is one of many wingless species.

logs, or in decaying bark or leaves. A few species, however, have invaded houses, bakeries, shops, and grocery stores, and eat almost anything. Their diets consist of animal and vegetable matter, garbage, and other insects. Cockroaches reproduce quickly in moist, dark places. They avoid bright light and usually search for food at night.

Generally, the female cockroach carries many eggs in a purse-shaped, hard-walled capsule, which she later hides in a damp, protected place. Once the eggs hatch, the young force their way out of the capsule. As the young cockroaches grow, they molt several times before becoming adults (see METAMORPHOSIS; MOLTING).

Cockroaches have been on Earth for millions of years. Fossil remains from the Carboniferous period have been found, indicating that cockroaches have changed very little in the past 300 million years.

COCONUT The coconut is the fruit of a tall palm tree. It is cultivated on sandy soil in tropical areas throughout the world. Reaching a height of 100 ft. [30 m], this palm has large leaves, 16.5 ft. [5 m] long, growing at the top of the tree (see PALM FAMILY). The coconut fruits grow in clusters among the leaves. Each fruit takes about a year to mature, and each tree can produce about one hundred fruits each year.

The coconut fruit is a seed enclosed in a woody shell that is in turn enclosed in a husk and rind. The seed itself is 8 to 12 in. [20 to 30 cm] long and 6 to 10 in. [15 to 25 cm] in diameter. It is made of sweet, white meat surrounded by a thin, brown skin. The hollow center is filled with coconut milk. Dried coconut meat is called copra. It can be shredded for use in a variety of foods or processed to produce an oil used for cooking and many other purposes.

In addition to the fruit, the coconut tree has other uses for humans. Its wood is used for buildings and furniture. The leaves and bark are used to make roofs, mats, and baskets. The husk of the fruit is used to make ropes and coconut matting. The sap is used to make sugar and an alcoholic beverage (drink).

COCONUT

Coconuts are often harvested by barefoot climbers. In some areas monkeys are trained to collect coconuts.

COCOON A cocoon is a silken covering for the pupa or chrysalis of various insects. The larva, which is the second stage in the life cycle of these insects, spins the cocoon just before it turns into the pupa. The pupa is the third stage in the life cycle and it eventually turns into the adult (see INSECT; LARVA; METAMORPHOSIS; PUPA). Cocoons are formed by the larvae or caterpillars of many moths. Some butterfly caterpillars also spin cocoons, and so do the larvae of bees, wasps, and ichneumon flies. Scraps of soil and plant material are often added to the cocoon to make it stronger or to make it less obvious to enemies. When the adult insect is developed, it bursts out of its pupal skin and then works its way out of the cocoon. Bees and wasps bite through their cocoons. Moths have no jaws, and many of them soften the cocoon silk with a special liquid before forcing their way out.

Adult spiders also spin silken cocoons in which they wrap their eggs. Worms wrap their eggs in cocoons as well, but these are made from the worms' skin and not from silk.

See also BUTTERFLY AND MOTH; CHRYSALIS; SILK-WORM MOTH.

COD A cod is a saltwater fish that belongs to the family Gadidae. This family of several species is a very important group of food fishes. Cod are widely distributed in deep, cold, northern waters. Cod may reach 6 ft. [1.8 m] in length and 200 lb. [91 kg] in weight, but most specimens are no more than about 3 ft. [1 m] long.

COD

The cod feeds on all kinds of sea creatures, including shrimps, prawns, and many smaller fishes.

COELACANTH (sē′lə kănth′) A coelacanth is a large saltwater fish that belongs to the family Coelacanthidae. The coelacanth was thought to be extinct until 1938, when a fisherman caught one in his nets off the coast of South Africa. Since then, a few of the primitive fish have been caught. Biologists do not know how common the coela-canth is because it lives in deep waters where nets cannot reach. Many fossil coelacanths have been found, showing that coelacanths were very numer-ous in the sea about 250 million years ago.

See also EXTINCTION; FOSSIL.

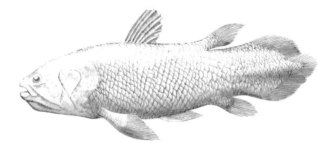

COELACANTH

Coelacanths have been around for over 350 million years, but were most common about 250 million years ago.

COELOM (sē′ləm) The coelom is the space in an animal's body between the outer tissue and the internal organs. It is also called the body cavity. In some animals, such as worms, it is full of fluid. In mammals, the coelom is separated into two parts by the diaphragm. The upper part, or chest cavity, contains the lungs and heart. The lower part, or abdominal cavity, contains the digestive organs.

COFFEE Coffee is a drink made from the roasted and ground beans (seeds) of the coffee plant. The plant, which is a shrub belonging to the Rubiaceae family, has glossy green leaves and white flowers. The shrub grows from 14 to 20 ft. [4.3 to 6.1 m] high, but most coffee growers prune it to 12 ft. [3.7 m]. It is cultivated in tropical climates in Asia, Africa, and the Americas. It grows best in upland areas.

Coffee plants are usually five years old before they begin to bear a full crop of coffee berries. The aver-age plant bears enough berries each year to make about 1.5 lb. [0.7 kg] of roasted coffee. Each berry contains two seeds.

Coffee contains caffeine, a drug that acts as a stimulant (see STIMULANT). The drug expands blood vessels so that more blood flows to the heart and brain. The result is that the coffee drinker feels less sleepy and more alert. However, many people

COFFEE

The ripe, red berries are picked mainly by hand and are often dried in the sun before the beans are taken out.

find that drinking coffee makes them feel nervous and causes them to have difficulty falling asleep when they want to. Many people drink decaffeinated coffee instead. This coffee has had its caffeine removed by chemical means.

COHESION Cohesion is the force that holds the molecules of a substance together. This force determines whether a substance is a solid, a liquid, or a gas. If the cohesion is strong, the molecules are tightly bound in place. The substance is then a solid. If the cohesion is very strong, the solid is hard. The cohesion is stronger in solids than in liquids. In gases, the cohesion is even less. For example, ice has a strong cohesive force and does not change shape easily. Water has a weaker cohesive force than ice. Its shape depends on the shape of its container. Steam has very little cohesion. It expands to fill its container. This shows that cohesion decreases as the temperature of a substance increases.
See also MOLECULE.

COKE Coke is a solid gray substance formed when coal is heated in an airtight oven, in a process called destructive distillation. The material that is volatile, or easily evaporated, is removed, leaving pores (little holes) in the coke (see DISTILLATION; EVAPORATION). Coke contains 87 to 89 percent carbon. Most coke produced is used for industrial purposes. Some of it is used to melt iron ore in a process called smelting. A small amount of coke is used as fuel.
See also COAL; COAL GAS; IRON; SMELTING.

COLD-BLOODED ANIMAL Animals whose body temperatures change according to their surroundings are called cold-blooded animals. Another term for them is *ectothermic* animals. The body temperature of a cold-blooded animal is nearly the same as the air around it. Cold-blooded animals, therefore, cannot survive in temperatures below freezing, for they would freeze. Cold-blooded animals that live in areas with cold winters usually hibernate in places that do not freeze, such as deep burrows or at the bottom of deep lakes (see

HIBERNATION). On hot, sunny days, cold-blooded animals must stay in the shade to prevent becoming too hot. Animals that live in deserts usually come out only at night. If the animals are too cold, they cannot move properly or find food, so on mild days, cold-blooded animals will "sun" themselves to raise their body temperature. Turtles are often seen sunning themselves on a rock in a pond.
See also WARM-BLOODED ANIMAL.

COLD, COMMON The common cold is the most widespread of all human diseases. It affects most people at some time in their lives. Many people suffer from colds several times a year, while others may "catch a cold" only once in several years. A cold is a viral infection of the upper respiratory tract, which includes the nose, sinuses, throat, and bronchial tubes. Since colds are caused by many different viruses, the body does not develop immunity to all of them, and it is possible to have a number of colds in a short period of time. Antibiotics do not kill viruses, and so do not cure colds (see ANTIBIOTIC; IMMUNITY; VIRUS).

The symptoms of a common cold vary from mild to moderate. These symptoms are the familiar sneezing and "runny" or "stuffy" nose and sometimes a cough or mild sore throat. Usually, if fever is present, it is mild. The mucous membranes in the throat and nose become swollen. Often, the bronchial tubes become inflamed. A person with asthma may have more symptoms from his or her asthma during a cold (see ASTHMA). A cold may last from twenty-four hours to two weeks or so.

A cold can be "caught" only from another person with a cold. When a person with a cold coughs or sneezes, he or she releases fine droplets that carry viruses into the air. These viruses may be inhaled by another person in the area and cause him or her to become infected.

There is no treatment for a cold virus, only for the symptoms. Aspirin or acetaminophen can help relieve body aches. Nasal sprays or decongestants taken by mouth can reduce the swelling of the mucous membranes, making it easier to breathe. There are many medications sold to treat the various other symptoms of a cold. At present, the best way to treat a cold is to rest, drink plenty of fluids (such as water or fruit juice), and take aspirin or acetaminophen as directed for mild fever or aches. Aspirin is not recommended for children, however, because there is a chance of getting a more serious illness called Reye's syndrome when aspirin is used during infection by certain viruses.

One of the major dangers of the common cold is that it weakens the body's defenses against other diseases. For example, an ear infection or pneumonia caused by bacteria may occur after a cold. A bacterial infection will usually require an antibiotic for treatment (see BACTERIA; INFECTION).

There have been several vaccines developed against the common cold, but none has been effective (see VACCINATION). Dr. Linus Pauling proposed that the use of vitamin C may be useful in preventing or treating a cold. His work has aroused much controversy (see PAULING, LINUS).
See also VITAMIN.

COLD FRONT

COLD FRONT A cold front is the surface along which a cold air mass meets a warm air mass (see AIR MASS; FRONT). Cold air is heavier and moves faster than warm air. The advancing cold air overtakes the warm air. The cold air then moves under the warm air, pushing the warm air upward. A steep slope of air masses is formed.

The upward movement of warm air produces thick, billowy forms called cumulus clouds (see CLOUD). Cumulus clouds sometimes develop into cumulonimbus clouds, or thunderheads (see THUNDERSTORM). Thunderheads cause the heavy precipitation that is usually associated with the passing of a cold front.

As cold fronts move across the United States, they usually move in a southeastward direction.
See also POLAR FRONT; WARM FRONT; WEATHER.

COLD FUSION

COLD FUSION Cold fusion is an experimental process in which the nuclei of hydrogen atoms join together (fuse) at comparatively low temperatures to form helium nuclei. High-temperature fusion powers the sun and stars and hydrogen-bomb explosions. Enormous amounts of light and heat are produced as fast-moving hydrogen nuclei smash into each other at temperatures of millions of degrees, and at pressures billions of times greater than the pressure of the earth's atmosphere. Scientists and engineers are trying to produce energy by a similar, controlled process, also requiring temperatures of millions of degrees. If low-temperature fusion could be achieved, it would be much cheaper and simpler.

Some scientists have claimed to produce cold fusion by chemical reactions in test tubes at labora-

COLD FRONT
A cold front occurs when a mass of cold air pushes under a mass of warmer air. As the warm air rises, its moisture condenses into clouds and falls as rain. Therefore, cold fronts are associated with unstable conditions and wet weather.

tory temperatures. They have observed subatomic particles, called neutrons, being produced by the reaction, which is normally a sign that fusion has occurred. But other scientists have not been able to repeat their result. Very few scientists in general believe that hydrogen-helium fusion is the reason for the appearance of neutrons.

In a more promising type of cold-fusion process, a special kind of hydrogen atom is used instead of hydrogen nuclei. In this atom, a particle called a muon replaces the single electron found in each normal hydrogen atom. The muonic atom is smaller than an ordinary hydrogen atom. This smaller size reduces the temperature needed to bring the nuclei close together. This process is still only experimental. *See also* ATOM; FUSION; NUCLEAR ENERGY; NUCLEAR WEAPONS.

COLLAGEN (kŏl′ə jən) Collagen is the most common protein in the human body (see PROTEIN). It is a tough, fibrous material found in bone, tendons, ligaments, cartilage, skin, and the dentin of teeth. Collagen fibers are made in the body by cells called fibroblasts.

The fibers form strands, something like pieces of rope, that are woven together in various ways to give strength and support to the different kinds of connective tissue (see CONNECTIVE TISSUE). The body requires vitamin C for the production of collagen (see VITAMIN).

The leather obtained from animal hides is tightly packed collagen. If collagen is boiled, it dissolves and forms gelatin. Collagen is widely used in the cosmetics industry. It is an ingredient in some shampoos, skin creams, and makeups. Manufacturers hope to convince the public that the application of collagen to hair and skin will make the hair stronger and the skin softer. This use has not yet been scientifically proven.

COLLENCHYMA (kə lĕng′kə mə) Collenchyma is a plant tissue whose cell walls are thickened with cellulose. These cells can lengthen to allow for growth of the plant. Collenchyma gives the plant strength and is usually found in young stems and leaves. It is the major source of support for herba-

ceous plants (plants with soft, green stems). In woody plants, the collenchyma is crushed as the woody tissue begins to form, and the cells gradually die.
See also CELLULOSE.

COLLOID (kŏl′oid′) A colloid is made up of tiny particles of one substance dispersed (spread evenly) in another substance. The particles are large single molecules or large groups of smaller molecules. The particles are extremely small, ranging in diameter from about 3 millimicrons (1 millimicron = 1 billionth of a meter) to about 4,000 millimicrons. All living things contain colloids (see MOLECULE).

Colloids can be made up of any combination of solids, liquids, and gases except gases combined with gases. A sol is a colloid of solid particles dispersed in a liquid. If the particles are dispersed in water, the colloid is called a hydrosol. Many solid-liquid colloids look like jelly. They are called gels. A colloid of liquid particles or droplets dispersed in another liquid is an emulsion. A dispersion of gas in a liquid is a foam. A colloid of solid or liquid particles in a gas is an aerosol. A colloid of a gas in a solid is a solid foam, such as foam rubber. Colloids of solid particles dispersed in solids can be made, such as ruby glass. Ruby glass consists of gold particles dispersed in glass (see EMULSION; SUSPENSION).

Colloids can be made by grinding or churning materials together until the tiny colloidal particles form. Some colloids are made by chemical reactions. Colloids can also be made by striking an electric arc between materials in a liquid.

A colloid may look like a solution. However, a beam of light shone through the liquid reveals the particles. This effect is not seen in a solution (see SOLUTION AND SOLUBILITY).

Colloids can be broken down into three main groups, according to their chemical behavior. Lyophobic, or "solvent-hating," colloids are not very stable (able to stay dispersed). Some remain stable only because of electric charges on the particles. The particles repel one another, therefore remaining dispersed.

Lyophilic, or "solvent-loving," colloids are more

stable. Lyophilic colloids are found in animal and plant fluids.

The molecules of association colloids have a hydrocarbon chain (see HYDROCARBON). This chain has a hydrophilic (water-loving) "head" group with a hydrophobic (water-hating) "tail" group. Such molecules form clusters called micelles. The micelles keep the head groups in contact with water. They also protect the tails from water within the micelle. Detergents and soaps are common examples of association colloids.

Most fluids in living things are colloids. Many products are colloids during manufacture, such as ceramics, cosmetics, foods, paints, papers, pesticides, and plastics.

COLOBUS The colobus monkey is a thumbless African monkey that lives in the tops of tall trees in tropical forests. It may grow as tall as 22 to 24 in. [55 to 60 cm] and has a tail that may be 34 in. [85 cm] long. There are several species, some red and some black and white. The guereza, or Abyssinian, colobus monkey is black with long, white fur around the face and on the tail. Colobus monkeys are plant eaters and have a stomach with several compartments, similar to that of ruminants (see RUMINANT).
See also MONKEY.

COLONIZATION Colonization is the gradual invasion, or taking over, of new areas or habitats by plants and animals. The island of Krakatoa was almost destroyed by a huge volcanic explosion in 1883. When people landed on the remains of the island two months later, they found that the ash covering it was still very hot. The island was declared lifeless, but after another nine months life began to return. Within 25 years the whole island was once again covered with plants.

A brand new island, called Surtsey, was formed by a volcanic eruption off the coast of Iceland in 1963. The island was lifeless at first, but birds soon started to roost on the barren rocks. Their droppings provided fertile spots in which plants could take root. Within four years plants had colonized much of the area along the coast. Their seeds could have floated across from the mainland, or they could have been blown by the wind or carried by birds.

If you have a garden, you can watch the process of colonization there. If you dig an area and leave it alone, it will soon be colonized by weeds that grow from seeds blown in by the wind or dropped by animals. As the plants get established, insects and other animals move in to feed on them. Only those species that find conditions to their liking will stay and grow well.

COLOBUS

A newborn guereza colobus monkey has white, curly fur. The coat begins to change to the straight black and white fur that is characteristic of adults when the monkey is five to ten months old.

Color is an aspect of light that allows humans and some animals to tell the difference between objects that are otherwise identical. The things we see all reflect certain wavelengths of light (see LIGHT). Eyes that have color vision contain structures that "see" different wavelengths of light as being different colors.

The light from the sun is commonly called white light. It is made up of all wavelengths or, as we see them, many colors put together. To show this, we can use a prism to break white light down into its spectrum of various colors. These are the colors we see in a rainbow. These same colors can be combined, using a second prism, back into white light (see PRISM; SPECTRUM).

When light reaches an object, some wavelengths are reflected (bounced back) and some are absorbed (taken in). The wavelengths that are reflected make up the color we see. If the skin of an apple reflects "red" wavelengths and absorbs all others, we see the skin as being red. A white object reflects practically all the light. A black object absorbs practically all the light (see ABSORPTION AND ADSORPTION).

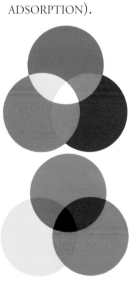

MIXING COLORS

In additive color mixing (top), primary colors combine to give white. In subtractive mixing (bottom), primary colors combine to give black. Paint samples (right) show a vast range of colors.

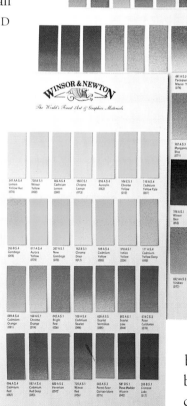

Any two or more colors of light can be combined to form another color of light. All colors of light mixed together make white light. This method of mixing colors is called the additive method.

Red, green, and blue are commonly called the primary colors of light for additive mixing. To demonstrate additive color mixing, one could put a red slide, a green slide, and a blue slide in three separate slide projectors. The next step would be to project the colors on a white surface and move them around so that the colors overlap slightly. When red and blue overlap, a color called magenta results. When blue and green overlap, a color called cyan is seen. When red and green overlap, yellow results. Color television depends on the principle of additive color mixture. Any color can be made by mixing light of the three primary colors in the right amounts.

When colors in pigments such as paints and dyes are mixed together, they combine differently from the colors of light. They do not combine additively, but rather subtractively. In additive mixing, more light is reflected as more colors are mixed. In subtractive mixing, more light is absorbed as more colors are mixed. When an artist uses pigments to paint a bowl of fruit, he or she is mixing the colors by the subtractive method. The artist can make any color needed using three primaries. With the subtractive method, the three common primaries are magenta, yellow, and cyan (blue green). For the painting, magenta and yellow could be mixed to paint reddish shades, or the color of an orange. Yellow and cyan could be mixed to get a green for grapes. For the black in the bowl, all three primary colors could be mixed together. As with the additive method, many other colors can be made by mixing the primaries in different amounts.

Two or more colors are said to be complementary to each other when they mix additively to form white or subtractively to form black. Green and magenta are complementary colors, and so are yellow and blue.

Several different systems of classifying colors have been developed. Color experts can describe a color using three terms: *hue, saturation,* and *brightness.* Hue is the basic name for the color—for example, red or blue. Saturation is the amount of hue in the color. "Fire-engine red" is highly saturated, but pink is not. Brightness tells us how light or dark the color is (see COLORIMETRY).

Using these terms, colors can be accurately described. In the United States, the National Bureau of Standards and the Inter-Society Color Council have devised a system for naming colors. They have named and standardized 270 different colors. These standardized colors are used in the textile industry, in the making of cosmetics, and in the standardization of house paints.

In nature, color is important for certain living things. It plays a role in the courtship behavior of many kinds of birds and fish. The coloration of

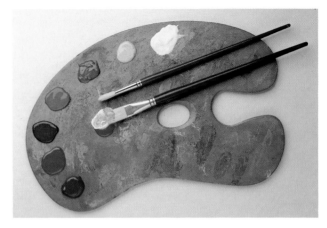

COLORED PAINTS
An artist generally uses just a few basic colors to mix all the colors he or she needs.

certain young animals enables them to blend in with natural settings, thus becoming almost hidden from their enemies (see CAMOUFLAGE). A blossom of a plant may attract certain bees or butterflies that will land on it. Then they will carry pollen to another flower for pollination and fertilization.

Some people have defective vision that prevents them from seeing certain colors (see COLOR BLINDNESS). Many animals cannot see color at all. Dogs, cats, horses, hogs, and many other animals live in a world of grays.

See also EYE AND VISION.

PROJECT 44, 52

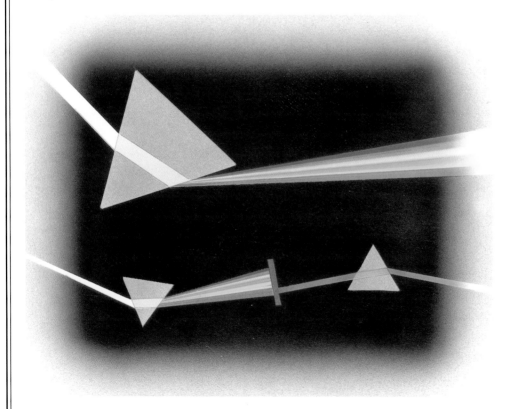

PRISMS
A prism splits white light into its spectrum of colors (top left). A second prism can combine the colors back into white light. If a colored filter is used to select a particular color in the spectrum produced by the first prism (bottom left), a second prism does not affect the selected color.

COLORADO POTATO BEETLE The Colorado potato beetle eats the leaves of potato plants. This beetle is also called the potato bug. It is about 0.5 in. [13 mm] long, with hard, yellow-and-black striped wing covers. The female lays clusters of eggs on potato leaves and these eggs produce pink larvae, which feed on the leaves for about three weeks. They then drop to the ground, bury themselves, and spend the next ten days developing into adults (see LARVA; METAMORPHOSIS). The insect can produce two or three broods or generations in a year. The adult beetles pass the winter buried in the soil.

Native to Mexico and the southwestern United States, the Colorado potato beetle was quite harmless until potatoes became an important crop in North America in the nineteenth century. Then it started to attack the potato crops and it spread rapidly, reaching the Atlantic coast by 1875. Farmers usually control the beetle with insecticides. *See also* BEETLE.

COLORADO POTATO BEETLE

This colorful beetle belongs to a group called leaf beetles. There are thousands of different beetles in this group and most of them feed on leaves. Many are serious crop pests.

COLOR BLINDNESS Color blindness, sometimes called Daltonism, is the lack of ability to tell colors apart. A person who is totally color-blind is said to have achromatic vision. Such a person sees the world only in shades of gray, white, and black, similar to a black-and-white photograph. Complete color blindness is very rare in humans (less than 1 in 30,000). Most mammals and many other animals are completely color-blind, but this condition is normal for their eyes.

Most people who are color-blind see only two main colors. They confuse all others. These people have dichromatic vision. For example, a person with dichromatic vision can usually see a difference between yellow and blue. The person may, however, confuse red with green. The person may also confuse some reds or greens with some yellows.

Many people do not know that they are color-blind. They have been raised and taught, for instance, to call a certain shade "red." They do not realize that they see this "red" differently than most people do. A person who is color-blind may be unaware of the condition and may easily place himself or herself in danger. For example, if the person confuses red and green, he or she may have a difficult time telling the colors of traffic signals apart.

People can be tested for color blindness. Both the Hardy-Rand-Ritter and Ishihara tests reveal the type and degree of color blindness. In these tests, colored squares, triangles, and other shapes lie within a heap of dots. These dots differ in color and brightness. A person tries to identify the colored shapes. His or her ability to do this determines his or her ability to see colors. The Holmgren test and Farnsworth Munsell 100 hue tests are used to test the ability of a person to match colors.

Color blindness can develop as a result of eye infection or eye damage. Usually color blindness is an inherited trait affecting the cones, which are the

ACTIVITY *Testing for color blindness*

Look at the above chart. Depending on your ability to see reds and greens, you will see either a cup or a teapot.

cells on the retina at the back of the eye that are sensitive to color (see EYE AND VISION).

The most common type of color blindness is a sex-linked (transmitted by genes located in the sex chromosomes) recessive (not dominant) trait. For example, a man who is color-blind and a woman with normal vision will have children with normal vision. The trait of color blindness is carried in the genes of the daughters of this couple (see CHROMOSOME; HEREDITY). These daughters can pass on the trait of color blindness to their own children. If a man who is color-blind has children with a woman whose father is color-blind, probably half of their children will be color-blind.

Almost five out of every one hundred men are color-blind, while only about one out of every two hundred women has this trait. There is no cure for color blindness to date.

See also COLOR; DALTON, JOHN.

COLORIMETRY (kŭl′ə rĭm′ĭ trē) Colorimetry
is the measurement of colors. Colors are distinguished by three characteristics: brightness, hue, and saturation (see COLOR). Since colors appear different to different people, even in the same light, color standards have been created. A color standard is the average judgment of many people on a certain color value. A color atlas contains a full range of color standards.

A colorimeter is a device that matches an unknown color with one that is made by mixing colored light, dyes, or coloring materials called pigments. In additive colorimeters, lights of primary colors are mixed in various amounts to make the final matching color. In subtractive colorimeters, color filters are used to subtract (remove) colors.

Since the human eye is not the most reliable color detector, it is often replaced in colorimetry by a photoelectric cell. This is an electronic device that produces an electric current or allows a current to flow when light shines on it (see PHOTOELECTRIC EFFECT). A photoelectric cell always gives the same reading for a particular color. Another colorimetric device is the spectrophotometer. It can be used to analyze a color that cannot be seen by the human eye.

See also SPECTRUM.

COMA A coma is a state of total loss of con-
sciousness from which a patient cannot be aroused. The word *coma* comes from a Greek word meaning "deep sleep." A coma may result from a head injury, poisoning, drug overdose, or certain disorders (see DIABETES). A person in a coma may have suffered some degree of brain damage, but more frequently, a coma is not permanent, and the person will awaken after treatment. A person in a coma should be kept warm and quiet until medical help arrives.

COLORIMETRY

Colorimetry is used in the textile industry to analyze the colors of fabrics and to study how they change when fabrics are washed or subjected to bright light.

Currently, the only way to treat coma is to treat the cause (for example, to give an antidote in the case of poisoning). Intensive-care measures are also used to make sure that the patient is breathing, that the blood is circulating well, and that he or she is receiving enough nutrition to support life while recovering. A coma may last from several seconds to many years.

COMBUSTION Combustion, or burning, is a chemical reaction that gives off light and heat. It can occur anytime there is rapid union of oxygen with other substances. When oxygen is plentiful during combustion, carbon dioxide is produced. When oxygen is scarce during burning, carbon monoxide is produced (see CARBON DIOXIDE; CARBON MONOXIDE). Oxygen, fuel, and heat are needed for combustion to continue. When any one of these is removed, the burning stops. People often think of combustion only in connection with oxygen-type fires, but combustion actually includes many other chemical reactions. For example, combustion occurs in the burning of any substance in chlorine, or when chlorine burns in hydrogen gas.

The ignition temperature is the lowest temperature at which a substance burns. The temperature of combustion is the highest temperature reached during combustion. The heat of combustion is the total amount of heat given off when a substance burns. It is measured in calories or joules (see CALORIE; JOULE).

Spontaneous combustion occurs when substances begin to burn without having been ignited by a match or some other burning object. Piles of oil-soaked rags or coal containing moisture sometimes begin to burn without having been ignited. The combustion, in this case, is caused by the rapid union of oxygen with hydrogen or carbon in the oil or coal. The rapid reaction raises the temperature above the kindling point, and the substances begin to burn.
See also FIRE.

PROJECT 6

COMER, JAMES PIERPONT (1934–) James Pierpont Comer is an African-American educator and psychiatrist. A psychiatrist is a medical doctor who specializes in the treatment of mental disorders (see PSYCHIATRY). Comer wrote several books on educating students in schools located in the inner city. The inner city is usually the older area of a large city. Many poor people often live in the inner city. Comer was born in East Chicago, Indiana, and attended medical school at Howard University in Washington, D.C. He received his medical degree in 1960. Comer then attended the University of Michigan, where he received a master's degree in public health in 1964. After working at the National Institute for Mental Health in Washington, D.C., he joined the child study center at Yale University in Connecticut.

At Yale, Comer developed an approach to education that stresses teacher support of students. Comer's approach also says schools should pay attention to a student's social and psychological needs as well as to his or her educational ones. This approach, which Comer calls the school development program, has been successful in schools in several states, including the public schools in New Haven, Connecticut. In 1990, the Rockefeller Foundation donated $15 million to efforts to use Comer's methods in schools around the United States. The Rockefeller Foundation is an organization that donates money to help solve world problems.

Some of Comer's most famous books include *Beyond Black and White, Black Child Care, School Power,* and *Maggie's American Dream.*

COMET A comet is a heavenly body that is a member of the solar system and has a distinct center and often a long, bright "tail." The center of the comet is probably made of dust, frozen gases, and ice. When the comet approaches the sun, the gases vaporize to form a cloud, called a coma, around the center (see VAPOR). The sunlight reflecting on the coma makes the comet visible.

As the comet moves closer to the sun, the smaller gas molecules and dust particles may be forced away from the coma, forming the tail of the comet. A comet may have two tails, one made of gas molecules and one made of dust particles. These tails always point away from the sun. On rare occasions,

COMET
This photograph of Comet Kohoutek was taken on January 11, 1974.

comets have periods of only a few years, while others have periods of thousands of years.

Comets develop tails and become bright only if they approach the sun. Astronomers believe there are millions of unseen comets circling the sun far beyond Pluto, the most distant planet. Sometimes comets are disturbed by passing stars, and may plunge into the inner solar system, circle around the sun, and travel out again. We see these comets just once, on the inner part of this journey. Other comets make regular appearances in our sky. The most famous is Halley's Comet, which has a period of approximately 76 years (see HALLEY'S COMET). Halley's Comet was last seen in 1986, and will be seen again in 2061. In late 1973, Comet Kohoutek became the first comet to be studied by astronauts in space, as part of the Skylab program of the United States.
See also SOLAR SYSTEM; SPACE EXPLORATION.

however, it might look as though one of these tails is pointing toward the sun. This "tail" is called an anti-tail. This illusion occurs when the earth and comet are aligned in a particular way. The tails of some comets are too short to be seen. Others are many millions of miles long. As comets disintegrate, they leave behind a trail of debris. When the earth passes through such a trail, meteor showers are observed (see METEOR).

Most comets follow an elliptical (oval-shaped) path around the sun. The time it takes a comet to make a complete orbit is called its period. Some

COMMENSALISM (kə mĕn′sə lĭz′əm) Commensalism is a type of relationship between organisms of two different species. One partner is helped by the relationship, and the other is not affected. Birds living in trees show a form of commensalism. The tree protects the bird that nests in its branches, but the tree is not hurt. Another type of commensalism is found between the remora and the shark. The remora is a small fish that clings to a shark and eats small pieces of food that the shark drops.
See also PARASITE; SYMBIOSIS.

COMMENSALISM
Small pilot fish often swim close to sharks. It was once thought that they helped to guide the sharks in some way, but they are probably just saving energy by "hitching rides" in the layer of water that moves forward with any large fish. They may also get scraps of food dropped by the sharks.

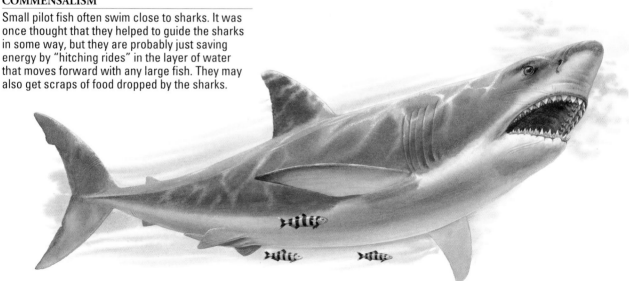

COMMUNAL ANIMALS

Most animals lead solitary lives and, except during the breeding season, the individuals have little contact with each other. A swarm of flies may gather on garbage, and a cloud of butterflies may descend on a patch of nectar-rich flowers, but each insect is seeking to satisfy its own needs and takes little notice of the others.

There are, however, quite a lot of animal species that regularly live together in some kind of social colony. These species are called communal animals or social animals. The individuals usually cooperate with each other to some extent, although this does not always happen. Fish schools, for example, keep together, but they have no leader and the individual fish can act independently. The advantage of keeping in a school is that it is less easy for a predator to pick out one fish and eat it—so there is safety in numbers. Huge groups of seabirds can be found on some cliffs during the breeding season, but the birds do not cooperate. They simply come together because they all need the cliffs for nesting.

Herds of bison and antelopes are rather loose groups with no obvious leaders or organization. The animals do not really cooperate with each other. Most colonies of mammals, however, are much more highly organized, with leaders who decide when and where the group will go and when the animals will feed or rest. Many of these colonies are really just large families. A beaver colony, for example, usually consists of a father and mother and their offspring, and all the members help with the work of building and repairing the nest and the dam (see BEAVER). As the youngsters grow up, they gradually move away from the family and start their own colonies.

Lion prides are small colonies, usually consisting of a number of females (lionesses) and their cubs, together with one or two adult males. The lionesses are often sisters and they help each other to bring up the cubs. The males guard the pride and defend the hunting territory. The females do most of the hunting, but the males are the rulers of the pride and they are the first to feed.

Monkeys and apes live in well-organized colonies. Each colony is usually ruled and protected by a big, strong male, and all the other individuals have their own places on the social scale.

MONKEY TROOPS

Chacma baboons are large African monkeys that live in troops containing as many as one hundred individuals. Each troop is dominated by a few large males. There is a well-established order within the troop, and because each individual knows its place, there is rarely any fighting.

LION PRIDES

The female lions in a pride are usually related to each other and there are strong bonds between them. They spend a lot of time grooming each other and they all help with the rearing of the cubs.

The animals quickly learn their places and always yield to those higher up on the scale, so there is rarely any fighting within the colony and they all live peacefully together. As a rule only the dominant males get to mate with the females. This is good for the colony because it means that the most powerful leaders pass on their qualities to the offspring and ensure good leaders for the next generation.

Most colonies of mammals stay in a particular area, although they do not necessarily have fixed homes within the area. Hunting colonies usually defend their areas against other colonies of the same species. The defended areas are called territories. Grazing animals often have overlapping areas, which are not defended against neighboring colonies. These areas are called home ranges.

The most complex colonies are found among the social insects—the ants and termites, and many bees and wasps. Many of these live in huge colonies, some of them with over a million individuals all working together for the good of the colony. Eggs are laid by one or a few females called queens, and most of the colony consists of workers. Each worker may have its own job, and some colonies produce different kinds of workers for different jobs. Some ants and termites, for example, have extra-large workers called soldiers that defend the colonies. Some workers take care of the nest or look after the young, while others go out to collect food. Workers may change jobs as they grow up. Honey bees, for example, spend several weeks working inside the nest before they are able to go out to collect pollen and nectar (see ANT; BEE; TERMITE).

PROJECT 73

ELEPHANT HERDS

African elephants live in herds of up to fifty animals. Each herd is led by an adult female, and all the females in a herd help each other to rear their babies. Adult males usually live alone or in small "bachelor herds."

COMMUNICATION

Communication is the exchange of information. Many organisms have developed some means of communication. For example, one-celled organisms such as the ameba move away from bright light. A simple response such as that is the most primitive type of communication: receiving information. Most members of the animal kingdom are able to communicate with one another by means of the senses (see SENSE). For example, fish can signal mates by releasing special chemicals called pheromones (see PHEROMONE). Bees perform complex dances to attract mates and to show where food can be found. Dogs bark to scare away an enemy. Skunks release a bad-smelling liquid to repel an enemy.

Even plants have means of communication. For example, if one leaf of a mimosa plant is touched, all the leaves fold up.

There are two basic types of communication. Internal communication is an organism's communicating with itself, such as the ameba or the mimosa plant. External communication is an organism's communicating with one or more other organisms.

SENSITIVE PLANTS

Mimosa pudica is called the sensitive plant. If a leaf is touched lightly, its leaflets fold up. If the disturbance continues, signals are sent to the rest of the plant, causing all the leaves to collapse.

External communication may be either personal or mass communication. In personal communication, an organism shares information with another organism. In mass communication, one or several organisms share information with many others.

Internal communication Internal communication occurs when a message, or stimulus, is received by an organism and is relayed to another part of that organism to cause a reaction, or response. For example, the stimulus of darkness causes some flowers to react by closing up. The earlier example of the mimosa plant shows a response to the stimulus of touch (see MOVEMENT OF PLANTS).

If a person touches a hot stove, he or she quickly moves his or her hand away. The stimulus of heat was received by the hand and processed by the brain. The brain "tells" the person to move his or her hand (see REFLEX).

Some machines are also able to communicate with themselves. For example, furnaces and air-conditioning systems shut themselves off when the room reaches a certain temperature (see THERMOSTAT). In an airplane, the automatic pilot compares the airplane's actual course with its planned course, and, if necessary, adjusts direction.

External communication In external communication, an organism shares information with another organism in one or more ways, all of which involve the senses. The media (means) involved may be gestures, vocal sounds, signals, pictures, or words. Gestures and vocal sounds are used by many animals, but the use of signals, pictures, and words seems limited to human beings.

Gestures may be body movements or facial expressions. Vocal sounds may be as simple as grunts and howls or as sophisticated as words. A signal is anything that warns or directs. Its advantage is that it allows communication over greater distances than do vocal sounds or gestures. Of course, a vocal sound or a gesture may also be a signal. For example, waving a hand may be a signal of friendship. Beacon fires and smoke signals were once used for communication over fairly long distances. Drums and trumpets also were used to signal or warn other people in an area.

Pictures found in prehistoric caves were probably meant as reminders of certain events, such as hunting or fishing. They may have been a way of teaching others how to do certain things. As these pictures became more exact and easier to use, they developed into words. Words are names given to things we see or know. Once words began to replace pictures as a medium of communication, language developed. Language is a regular way of using words so they can be understood by the people in a certain group. As language became more popular, a way of recording it—writing—developed.

Personal communication The most basic methods of communication between people are vocal sounds, facial expressions, and body gestures. It was thousands of years between the time that people began to talk and the time that they began to write. Before 3000 B.C., the Egyptians had developed a scheme, called hieroglyphics, for writing their language. At first, hieroglyphics were based on pictures drawn to represent things. Later, the drawings were simplified to represent sounds in the language. By A.D. 500, hieroglyphics were no longer in use.

SNOW FLAGS

Flags are often used to communicate information in sports. This black-and-yellow checkered flag is flown on ski slopes to warn skiers of the danger of an avalanche.

FACIAL EXPRESSIONS

Facial expressions are an important method of communication between apes. This male barbary ape is opening and closing his mouth as he holds a young ape. An open mouth or fixed stare is often a sign of aggression. Pursing lips or pouting is often a sign of friendliness.

In about 1500 B.C., the Semites of Syria and Palestine had developed an alphabet. Their alphabet had about twenty simple pictures that stood for different sounds. This greatly simplified writing, as the people no longer had to learn a separate symbol for each word. The new symbols could be combined to represent any word in the language. The idea of an alphabet was continued by the Greeks and Romans. They further simplified the letter symbols by making them easier to write. The alphabet has been adapted to the familiar English alphabet now in use in the United States and many other countries.

With the increased use of the alphabet, more people learned to read and write. Stone tablets were replaced by primitive types of paper, making writing easier. Libraries were established around 600 B.C. by the Assyrians and the Babylonians. Messenger and postal service became more efficient, so people were able to communicate over fairly long distances.

The greatest advances in personal communication came about after the discovery and control of electricity (see ELECTRICITY). Samuel Morse used

HIEROGLYPHICS

By 3000 B.C., the ancient Egyptians had developed a type of writing called hieroglyphics. In this system, picture symbols represented sounds or whole words, such as the symbol for water (bottom left).

principles of electromagnetism to develop the telegraph in 1844. Because the telegraph was only able to make clicking sounds, Morse also developed a code to be used for communication. The Morse code uses dots (short clicks) and dashes (long clicks) to represent the letters of the alphabet (see MORSE, SAMUEL; TELEGRAPH). In 1876, Alexander Graham Bell invented the telephone, making it possible for people to communicate by voice over long distances (see BELL, ALEXANDER GRAHAM; TELEPHONE).

Until the 1900s, the major problem with the telegraph and telephone was that they required wires between the communicating units. In the late 1890s, Guglielmo Marconi invented a wireless telegraph.

A wireless telephone, or radio telephone, was invented in 1900. The radio telephone allowed people to communicate with each other over great distances, without the use of connecting wires. Some developments from the original radio telephone are commercial broadcast radio, amateur radio, citizen's band radio, and emergency two-way radio used by police officers, fire fighters, and others (see MARCONI, GUGLIELMO; RADIO).

Electricity was also a key factor in the phonograph, invented in 1877 by Thomas Alva Edison. The phonograph was the first instrument that was able to record voices (see EDISON, THOMAS ALVA). In the early 1820s, photography was invented, but it was not until 1884 that a flexible transparent film was developed by George Eastman. In 1889, Edison invented motion pictures. In 1923, the first motion pictures with sound were introduced. These advances led to the development of television in the 1920s and its introduction to the public in 1936 (see MOTION PICTURE; PHOTOGRAPHY; TELEVISION).

Mass communication As early people began to communicate on a one-to-one basis, they wanted to share information with many people in many places. As a result, forms of mass communication were developed. Mass communication is a way to learn about the world and what events are occurring. It is a way of passing information from one generation to the next. It is a way for a person to be informed and entertained so that he or she can make choices and decisions based on many facts instead of just a few.

In the eighth century A.D., the Chinese and others started using wood blocks to print books. It was

DISH ANTENNA

Dish-shaped antennae are used to communicate by radio over long distances. Radio energy is received over the whole face of the dish and reflected onto a detector held above it. Radio signals transmitted via a dish are formed into a beam that can be sent in any direction by turning the dish.

not until about A.D. 1440, however, that a machine was invented that completely changed the way books were printed. Johannes Gutenberg invented a printing press that used movable metal type. This made it much easier and less expensive to print books and other material. By the 1600s, newsletters had become common. In 1783, daily newspapers were begun in Philadelphia.

As printing methods improved, costs decreased. More people were able to afford newspapers, books, and magazines. As more people learned to read, they became more interested in the government. Free public education was introduced, and it became necessary to be literate (able to read and write) in order to keep in touch with the rapidly changing events of the day. When Gutenberg introduced the printing press, fewer than 10 percent of the people in the world were literate. Today, in the United States, 80 percent of all adults are literate. People in the United States spend billions of dollars every year on printed material (see PRINTING).

Radio and television broadcasts are probably the most popular forms of mass communication. The average home in the United States has several radios. More than 95 percent of the automobiles have radios. More than 98 percent of the people have at least one television set in their homes. Through these media, millions of people can be contacted at one time. Radio and television bring news, sports, entertainment, and education into

PORTABLE RADIOS
Walkie-talkies are small, two-way radios. They are employed where telephones cannot be used, such as on large construction sites.

the home so that people can receive these communications conveniently. This is important for warnings of bad weather or other dangers. It is also vital to a government whose leaders must stay in contact with the people.

Information age At the opening of the twentieth century, the amount of information available was doubling about every one hundred years. Today, it is doubling about every four years, largely because of the computer. The rate of information buildup is likely to increase because each technical advance opens a door to other new applications and refinements.

Most of the information systems in use today share a common base—computers. Modern computers make it possible to store and process huge amounts of information. They also allow users to share that information with many other users. A device called a modem allows information to be sent from computer to computer over telephone lines. Modems also allow a user to receive such information as stock market prices and weather information. A large group of users who communicate using modems make up a network (see COMPUTER; MODEM).

Another modern way to communicate is through a facsimile machine (see FACSIMILE MACHINE). Facsimile machines transmit copies, or faxes, of handwritten or typed material, maps, photographs, or drawn art over telephone lines to another facsimile machine. The process of transmitting information by a facsimile machine takes about the same time as it does to complete a telephone call.

Communicating by telephone has become more convenient with the invention of portable telephones. Portable telephones can be carried from room to room in a house, or used in a car (see TELEPHONE). Workers at airports and large construction sites can communicate with each other using small walkie-talkie radios (see RADIO).

Communication today has entered a whole new era. People can share information more quickly and inexpensively than ever before. Many hope these advancements will lead to a greater understanding among people all over the world.

COMMUTATOR A commutator is a device that is used to reverse the direction of electric field in a direct current (DC) generator or motor. A commutator usually consists of a cylindrical ring of insulated conducting elements mounted on a shaft. The shaft is connected to the armature, another cylindrical device containing coils of wire. As the armature rotates inside the field structure, which is a group of magnets or electromagnets, it generates alternating current (AC), which is current that reverses direction every half turn of the armature. The current then flows to the commutator, which is also rotating. The commutator changes the alternating current into direct current, which is current that moves in only one direction. The current is picked off the commutator by carbon graphite sticks, called brushes, that rub against it. The current then flows out of the generator or motor to its external destination.

See also ALTERNATING CURRENT; DIRECT CURRENT; DYNAMO; ELECTRIC MOTOR; ELECTROMAGNETISM; GENERATOR, ELECTRICAL.

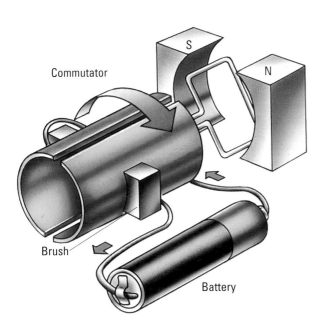

COMMUTATOR

This commutator is the part of a DC motor that reverses the direction of the electric current in the rotating coil every half turn of the coil. In the simplest DC motor with one rotating coil, the commutator is a metal ring split into two halves, each insulated from the other. In practice, a DC motor has many coils, so the commutator is divided into many smaller segments.

COMPASS A compass is a device used for determining direction by means of a magnetic needle. The compass is used to navigate on land, at sea, or in the air (see MAGNETISM; NAVIGATION).

A compass has markings that show the four main directions—north, south, east, and west—as well as various points in between. The magnetic needle of the compass always points north and south due to the pull of the earth's magnetic poles (see MAGNETIC POLE).

A simple pocket compass is useful to a hiker, especially when there are no landmarks for guidance. The hiker first needs to know the direction his or her destination is. For example, if his or her camp is east, the compass shows what direction east is in relation to where the hiker is standing. The hiker then heads east, periodically checking the heading by means of the compass.

The Chinese were the first to develop the compass, about eight hundred years ago. Their compass had a piece of lodestone, which is a naturally magnetized mineral, hanging from a string (see LODESTONE). The ends of the stone pointed to the north and the south. The Portuguese improved the compass for travel on sea in the late 1300s. They placed the compass in a glass case, called a binnacle, for protection. The binnacle was then mounted on a gimbal (frame) to keep the compass steady when

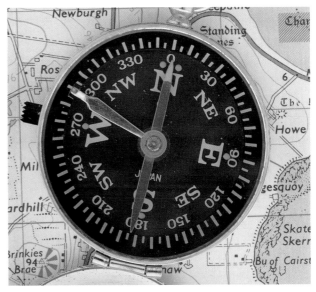

COMPASS

To use a compass to line up a map, turn the compass so that the swinging needle points to the compass's north and lines up with north as indicated on the map.

the sea was rough. Other improvements were made to the compass over the years. Navigators found that if a compass was placed near a metal object, the magnetic needle was pulled toward that object. The angle that represents the difference between the north–south line and the direction the compass points because of the pull of the object is called deviation. Magnets were placed inside the binnacle to help correct for deviation. Navigators also have to adjust for declination. Declination is the angle that represents the difference between geographic north and magnetic north. Navigators use charts that show what kind of adjustments have to be made in reading the compass.

Today's ships, aircraft, and spacecraft often have electronic compass systems. In such a system, compasses are corrected for deviation and declination by computers. Ships, aircraft, and spacecraft also use a device called a gyrocompass, which uses gyroscopes rather than a magnetic needle (see GYROSCOPE).　　　　PROJECT 28, 37

COMPOSITE FAMILY
The composite family is the largest and most highly evolved family of flowering plants. It includes more than twenty thousand species of herbs and shrubs (see HERBACEOUS PLANT). Members of the composite family are found throughout temperate and tropical areas of the world.

The leaves vary in size and may be simple or compound (see LEAF). They may alternate on the stem or form a rosette on the ground.

Each of the flowerheads of the composite family

COMPOSITE FAMILY—Asters
This garden aster, like many cultivated composites, has been specially bred to produce lots of extra-large florets.

COMPOSITE FAMILY—
Different family members
The sunflower, chicory, and mutisia all belong to the composite family. Some sunflower heads grow to be well over 12 in. [30 cm] across and contain hundreds of individual flowers, or florets.

Sunflower

Chicory

Mutisia

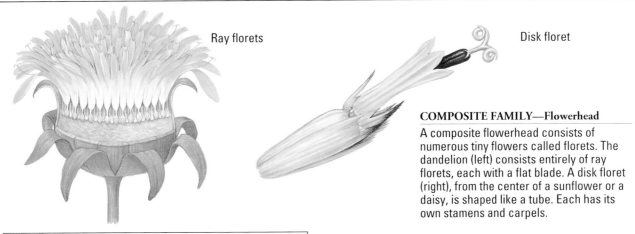

Ray florets

Disk floret

COMPOSITE FAMILY—Flowerhead
A composite flowerhead consists of numerous tiny flowers called florets. The dandelion (left) consists entirely of ray florets, each with a flat blade. A disk floret (right), from the center of a sunflower or a daisy, is shaped like a tube. Each has its own stamens and carpels.

ACTIVITY *Watching seeds disperse*

Find a fluffy seed head of a dandelion or some similar plant and look at the feathery "parachute" on top of each seed. Blow hard at the parachutes and watch them drift away. See how far they travel.

COMPOST Compost is a mixture of organic wastes, such as those from a kitchen or yard, that have been allowed to decompose or rot. Compost is added to soil as a fertilizer. Wastes in compost can include grass clippings, leaves, coffee grounds, and apple cores. Once the compost is added to soil, microorganisms in the soil break down the wastes so that the nutrients in them can enter the soil. Many homeowners make their own compost and use it on their lawns, gardens, and trees. Compost fertilizes these areas without using artificial chemicals. Compost also disposes of wastes without filling up dumps and landfills.
See also FERTILIZER; HUMUS; MICROORGANISM.

PROJECT 75

COMPOST
Compost can be made simply by making a pile of kitchen and yard wastes in the garden. But the material rots more quickly and makes better compost if it is put in a special compost box that keeps the warmth in.

is actually made up of many small florets packed tightly together. There are two kinds of florets in most composite flowers. In the sunflower, for example, ray florets form the yellow, outer fringe, and disk florets make up the inner brown disk (see FLOWER).

Members of the composite family produce many seeds and have effective means of dispersal (see DISPERSION OF PLANTS). Some seed coverings, such as those of thistle and dandelion, have lightweight, feathery hairs for wind dispersal. Other seeds have bristles or burrs so they will stick to an animal's fur.

Plants in the composite family have many uses. Chrysanthemums and asters are grown for their brightly colored flowers. Chicory, lettuce, and artichokes are grown for use as human food. Some plants, such as calendula and tansy, are used in medicines. The compass plant and goldenrod are two common wildflowers in this family.

COMPOUND A compound is a chemical substance made up of two or more different elements. In a compound, the atoms of the elements are linked together by chemical bonds. In this way, they form a completely different substance. For example, hydrogen (H) and oxygen (O) are both colorless gases. If a chemical reaction occurs between them, they can combine to form water (H_2O). In a compound, elements act differently than they do alone. The elements that make up a certain compound are always in the same ratio (see ATOM; ELEMENT).

There are thousands of different compounds. Many occur in nature, and many are made by chemists who put elements or other compounds together (see CHEMICAL REACTION). PROJECT 16

COMPRESSOR A compressor is a machine that increases the pressure of air by reducing its volume (see BOYLE'S LAW). Compressors are also used to compress other gases and liquids. There are two main types of compressors: piston and rotary. The piston compressor is the most widely used type. It consists of a piston that moves up and down inside a cylinder, much like a piston in an internal combustion engine. The crankshaft of a gasoline, diesel, or electric engine moves the piston up and down. As the piston moves to the bottom of the cylinder, air is drawn into the vacated space above it. When the piston rises to the top of the cylinder, it compresses ("squeezes") the air in the cylinder, and a special valve releases it into a rubber tube or hose. Some commercial tools, such as pneumatic drills that are used to break up rocks and pavement, and power wrenches used in auto tire garages, require extra high-pressure compressed air. Compressors with several cylinders are used to generate this additional pressure. The compressed air flows from cylinder to cylinder and gets an additional boost in pressure each time it is recompressed.

The rotary type of compressor is not as efficient as the piston type. It consists of a rotating fan, called an impeller, that pushes air through metal passages arranged in a spiral pattern. The air passages are wide where the air enters and narrow where it comes out. This causes the air flowing through the passages to be compressed.

Compressed air is also used as the propelling force in commercial insecticide sprayers and paint sprayers. It is available at most gasoline stations free of charge for filling rubber tires on vehicles. Compressed air is used to pressurize the suits and helmets of deep-sea divers and to operate braking systems on large trucks and railway trains. Small hand pumps are available for home use to fill bicycle tires and sports equipment.

Gas turbine jet engines used in airplanes have axial-flow air compressors that compress air for combustion (burning). Axial flow means that the airflow through the compressor is parallel to the main axis of the engine. These compressors consist of a series of alternating fixed and moving blades inside a cylindrical housing. The blades at the front end, where the air enters, are shorter and farther away from the housing than the blades at the rear end, which are longer and very close to the housing. The blades are designed to push the air toward the rear where it is compressed.

Refrigerators contain compressors that compress refrigerant liquids and liquefied gases. The compressed liquids are released into a series of closed tubes, where they become gases and extract heat from the inside of the refrigerator in the process (see REFRIGERATION).

COMPUTED TOMOGRAPHY Computed tomography, also called CT scanning or CAT scanning, is a medical procedure used to diagnose disorders. CT scanning uses a computer and X rays to create precise images (CT scans) of separate overlapping organs on a computer screen or paper. The images are detailed "slices" of the anatomy.

CT images show the liver and kidneys better than do film X rays and are useful in looking at the brain and abdomen. CT images can show the size and location of abnormal growths, called tumors, as well. In some cases, a colorless liquid, called a contrast agent, is given to the patient so the medical team can better see the organs being studied. CT examinations are done by technologists. The images are interpreted by a radiologist, a physician who specializes in the use of radiation for diagnosis and treatment.

See also RADIOGRAPHY; X RAY.

A computer is an electronic device that can perform complex tasks, including problem solving, quickly and accurately. There are different kinds of computers, but each performs the same basic task. Data (information)—both words and numbers—are inputted (entered) into the computer. The computer then manipulates the data by following programs, or sets of instructions. The computer then outputs (gives out) its results.

A computer is able to perform a wide variety of tasks simply by following different programs. The programs used by a computer are referred to as software. For example, many people use computers when they write letters, reports, books, and magazine articles. The programs needed to manipulate words to accomplish such tasks are called word processing programs. The computers that can perform word processing can also use other software to draw pictures and carry out accounting procedures. In each of these cases, the actual computer, or the hardware, remains the same.

Computers have many other uses. Architects and engineers use a process called computer-aided design (CAD) to make detailed drawings of buildings and bridges very quickly. Previously, all such drawings were made by hand on paper, using such drafting instruments as compasses and protactors (see MECHANICAL DRAWING). Factories use a process called computer-aided manufacturing (CAM) to have machines do work previously performed by humans, such as assembling parts on a car (see AUTOMATION; ROBOTICS). Computers are used in medicine to study and treat the body. For example, in computed tomography, computers and X rays help doctors diagnose disease (see COMPUTED TOMOGRAPHY).

In business, computers are used to monitor inventory and payroll records and maintain information on clients. In music, composers use computers to help them write music and assign notes to specific instruments in an orchestra. In publishing, computers are used to arrange words and graphics in a process called desktop publishing. Computers are also becoming more widespread in the home as a way to keep track of household records and also for playing computer games.

History of computers The first machine used to solve mathematical problems was the abacus (see ABACUS). The abacus is a wooden frame that has beads strung on wires between two of its sides. The beads stand for numbers and can be moved to perform different calculations. The abacus is thousands of years old. It is still in use in some countries.

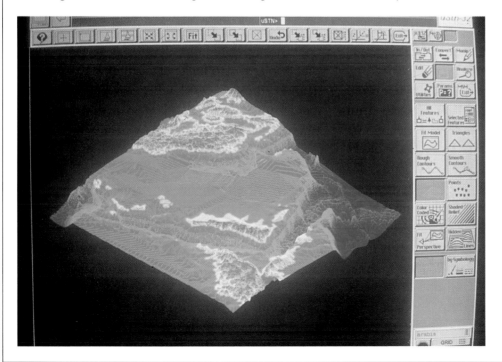

COMPUTER-GENERATED IMAGES

Maps, graphs, and pictures are much easier to understand than numbers. A computer can transform thousands of numbers into a more meaningful three-dimensional graph, map, or picture. Engineers and scientists use computer-generated images like this to help them understand complex problems.

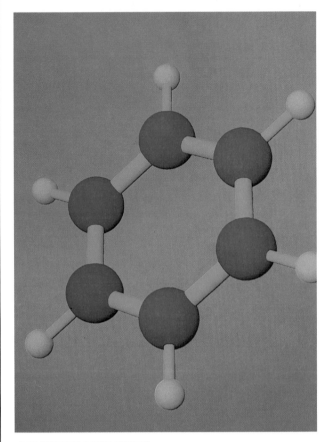

COMPUTER MODELING
Scientists use computers to create 3-D models of molecules in the computer's memory. The models can be viewed from any angle on the computer's screen. Scientists use these models to study the structure of molecules and how different molecules fit together when they interact with each other.

During the 1830s, the English mathematician Charles Babbage invented the first modern calculating machine. Babbage called his invention the "analytical engine." It was designed to do complicated calculations according to instructions in the form of punched cards and store the results at each stage of the calculation. However, the machine never worked properly because manufacturing techniques were not advanced and precise enough. Babbage's invention may have failed, but his ideas formed the foundation of all modern computing (see BABBAGE, CHARLES).

It was not until the late 1930s that the first simple electronic digital computer appeared. A digital computer is a computer that converts all inputted information, including words, into digits. The converted information is referred to as digital information. This first electronic digital computer was built by John Atanasoff, a mathematics professor at

Iowa State College, and his assistant, Clifford Berry. Atanasoff decided to invent his own calculating device when existing devices could not handle the computations he needed to perform for his doctoral and master's students. Meanwhile, in Britain, the first programmable all-electronic computer called Colossus was built in great secrecy in 1943 to break secret German military codes. The Atanasoff-Berry Computer (ABC) was the foundation for ENIAC (electronic numerical integrator and calculator), the first large-scale electronic digital computer. ENIAC was built in 1946 by a team of engineers at the University of Pennsylvania. ENIAC had 18,500 vacuum tubes, 70,000 resistors, 10,000 capacitors, and 6,000 switches (see CAPACITOR AND CAPACITANCE; RESISTOR; VACUUM TUBE). It occupied the space of a two-car garage. When it was first operated, many of ENIAC's parts repeatedly burned out. It was difficult for the computer to operate for more than seven or eight minutes. Gradually, the machine was improved to the point that it could make as many as five thousand additions and subtractions a minute. Although the ENIAC and the ABC were very slow by modern standards, they led the revolution in computers.

Key advancements Computers have progressed dramatically since the days of ENIAC. Since the late 1940s, scientists and engineers have created computers that are increasingly faster, smaller, and less expensive. This progress has been due largely to the development of two kinds of electronic devices: transistors and integrated circuits (ICs). A transistor is an electronic device used to control and amplify an electric signal. An integrated circuit consists of various tiny components that act like other electronic components, such as capacitors, resistors, and transistors. The components are located on a small chip of silicon. The silicon acts as a semiconductor (see INTEGRATED CIRCUIT; SEMICONDUCTOR; TRANSISTOR).

The transistor largely replaced the vacuum tubes of ENIAC and other early computers. Transistors do not burn out as often, are faster, require less electricity to run, and do not give off the huge amounts of heat that vacuum tubes do. By the mid-1950s,

EARLY COMPUTERS

The first large-scale electronic computers were built in the 1940s and 1950s. They used thousands of vacuum tubes, resistors, capacitors, and switches, all linked by miles of wires.

MAGNETIC DISKS

The largest computers are known as mainframes. Programs and data used by mainframe computers are often stored on magnetic disks or reels of magnetic tape like the one being held by this computer operator.

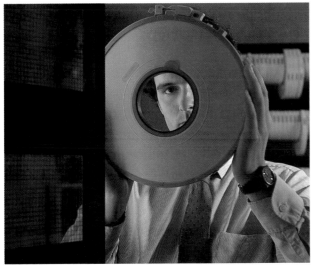

transistors were allowing scientists to produce "second-generation" computers that were not only faster, but smaller, cheaper, and more reliable than any previous computer. However, it was not long before transistors were replaced by another component that was smaller and more powerful yet—the IC.

The development of ICs in 1958 made possible yet another generation of still faster and more powerful computers. ICs and other computer components are often referred to as chips because they contain thousands of tiny electronic components that are packed closely together on chips of silicon (see CHIP). Some of today's ICs are so tiny that they can pass through the eye of a needle. Others are the

size of a fingernail. These tiny chips contain many more components than the room-sized computers of the 1940s and 1950s.

ICs have many uses in a computer. One of the uses is to contain the memory of the computer. ICs also control the parts of the computer that perform such tasks as adding, subtracting, and sorting and comparing data. All these functions are usually combined into one complex IC, called a microprocessor. Microprocessors are widely used in such devices as calculators, cars, video games, and videotape recorders (see CALCULATOR; VIDEO RECORDING).

Most of the computers used today are digital computers. Digital computers operate through circuits that are either switched on or switched off. A circuit that is switched on allows electricity to flow. A circuit that is switched off does not allow electricity to flow. These circuits translate words or numbers into the digits zero and one. Zero and one make up the binary number system (see BINARY NUMBERS). The information signified by each zero and one is called a bit. An eight-bit series is called a byte. Different computers have different byte capacities.

Types of computers Any computer is one of three main types. The first type is the mainframe. Mainframes are very large, powerful computers

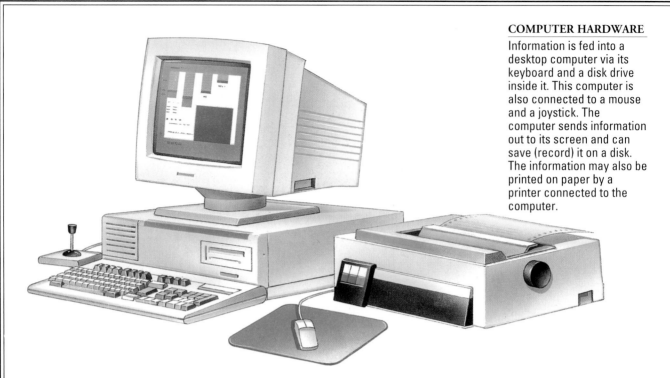

COMPUTER HARDWARE
Information is fed into a desktop computer via its keyboard and a disk drive inside it. This computer is also connected to a mouse and a joystick. The computer sends information out to its screen and can save (record) it on a disk. The information may also be printed on paper by a printer connected to the computer.

that can make many millions of complex calculations per second. They are used to solve the most complex problems, such as plotting the course of a satellite through space or manipulating large amounts of data, such as tax or census records of large numbers of people. Many different users can use the mainframe at the same time. The largest and fastest mainframes are called supercomputers. Computer users away from the office can communicate with the mainframe by using modems to send information over telephone lines. The baud rate determines how fast this communication occurs. Modems allow people away from the office to communicate not only with the mainframe, but with co-workers, both those who are in the office and others who are away from the office. Information sent over the modem is often referred to as "electronic mail." A large group of computer users who communicate using modems make up a network. By becoming a part of a certain network, a computer user can receive such information as stock market prices and weather information (see BAUD; MODEM).

A second type of a computer is a minicomputer. Minicomputers are not as fast or as powerful as mainframes, but they can still perform very complex tasks, such as keeping track of inventory in a large business.

The third type of computer is the microcomputer. A microcomputer is often called a personal computer. Because of recent advancements in the ability of microcomputers to solve complex problems, they are widely used in business, education, government, and scientific research. Many families also use microcomputers at home for entertainment or to keep track of household records. Microcomputers are now able to do tasks that once only minicomputers could do. Battery-operated portable models called "laptops" or "notebook computers" and even smaller "pocket" microcomputers are also gaining in popularity.

Portable computers are especially popular among reporters and traveling business people who need to use a computer away from the office. Modems allow them to communicate with other computer users or with a mainframe.

Parts of a computer Generally, all digital computers work the same way because they have the same basic components: input, storage, processing, and output devices. The input devices convert information into a form the computer understands. Input devices include keyboards, a device called a "mouse," graphic pens and tablets, touch screens, and optical scanners. Keyboards allow the user to directly type information into the computer. A mouse directs a pointer to select specific instructions. The instructions appear on a video display unit that resembles a television screen. A graphic tablet is used for drawing. The user "draws" on the pad with the pen. However, the sketch appears on the screen rather than the pad. Touch screens allow the user to select instructions by touching where they appear on the screen. Optical scanners convert handwritten or printed material into electrical signals. Many stores use optical scanners and bar codes to record the prices of items purchased. Some computers are even able to convert spoken words into a language the computer understands.

Storage devices include disks and disk drives. There are two types of disks—a floppy disk and a hard disk. A floppy disk is a small, flexible, plastic disk that is coated with magnetic material and enclosed in a thin case. Information is recorded on floppy disks as magnetic signals. A floppy disk can be easily carried from computer to computer. A hard disk resembles a floppy disk but is made of a rigid substance. A hard disk usually is located inside the computer and is not removed by the user. Because of their design, hard disks can store more information than floppy disks. A reading head is positioned over the floppy or hard disk and retrieves information from the disk. The information is stored by the disk drive in preparation for processing.

Another type of disk that is gaining in popularity is the optical disc. Optical discs are becoming more popular because they can store much more information than a floppy or a hard disk can. Optical discs resemble compact discs (see SOUND RECORDING). Information is recorded on these disks as a series of pits and ridges. The information is retrieved by a laser located inside a drive. Some optical discs are referred to as being "read only." This means that new information cannot be recorded on them. Optical discs that can be read as well as store new information are referred to as being "read/write" disks.

Inside the computer, the inputted information is first handled by a chip or set of chips called the central processing unit, or CPU (see CPU). The CPU matches the information with the program that the user requested for that particular task. The program is stored on either a floppy disk or hard disk. The CPU loads the program into its memory where the actual manipulations occur. There are two types of memory: read-only memory (ROM) and random-access memory (RAM).

The ROM is established when a computer is made. The ROM contains instructions for the computer on how to operate. The computer can read these instructions, but it cannot change or erase them. For example, the ROM contains instructions on what language to use. The ROM of a computer used in Japan would tell it to use

COMPUTERS' USES
Computers are often used to monitor and control machines. These computers control the flow of oil between an oil field and a refinery in Kuwait.

LAPTOP COMPUTERS

The miniaturization of electronic circuits made it possible to build computers small enough to sit on the user's lap. Notebook computers like the model shown here are even smaller than laptop computers. The smallest computers of all are called palm-top computers because they are small enough to hold in a person's hand.

Japanese letters. The RAM is short-term memory. This means it can be changed. The information from the input devices, the program, and the manipulations that the computer performs are stored in the RAM. Another set of instructions works with the memory of the computer. These instructions are referred to as the disk operating system (DOS). The DOS is similar to the ROM in that it tells the computer how to operate. However, instructions in the DOS can be changed. For example, the DOS might contain instructions that allow the computer to operate with a different kind of printer attached to it.

After the memory has processed the information, the CPU conveys the information to the user through an output device. One kind of output device is a video display unit (VDU). Printers, which produce written information on paper, are another output device. Information may be output directly to another computer user through a modem. Some computers even speak their results through a device called a voice synthesizer.

Other important parts of every computer are the clock and the power supply. The clock is controlled by a quartz crystal that vibrates at a rate of many millions of times a second. These vibrations control the exact rate at which the computer's activities occur. The faster the vibrations, the faster the calculations.

The power supply provides the computer with the exact amount of power it needs to run properly.

A typical application of a computer is to write a letter. The process begins when the user selects a word processing program. The user then inputs the information, in this case, words, by using a keyboard. As the user types, the information is converted into digits. Almost simultaneously, the computer outputs the information onto the screen for the user to view. Any manipulations performed on that letter, such as deleting or moving words or paragraphs, occur in the RAM on instructions from the program. When the user is finished with the letter, the letter can be stored on a floppy disk or hard disk. The letter can be outputted in other forms, also. For instance, it can be printed on paper or sent over the modem to another user.

Computers can be thought of as part of an ongoing revolution. Scientists are researching ways to allow the computer to store and manipulate larger and larger amounts of information. Research is sure to continue in the area of computers understanding human speech. Artificial intelligence is another area of great possibilities. Artificial intelligence involves programming computers so that they can "think," "reason," and "learn" from their mistakes as humans do (see ARTIFICIAL INTELLIGENCE). *See also* ELECTRONICS.

CONCAVE The term *concave* refers to a surface that curves inward at the center. The inside of a bowl is an example of a concave surface. A lens that is concave is thinner at the middle than it is at the edges.
See also CONVEX; LENS.

CONCAVE

A concave lens, above, is curved like the inner surface of a bowl.

CONDENSATION

This window is misted by condensation. When warm, moist air meets a cold window, water vapor in the air condenses on the glass as water droplets.

CONDENSATION Condensation is the change of a substance from a gas to a liquid. Condensation occurs when the temperature of a gas drops below its boiling point. For example, steam condenses to water when it is cooled below its boiling point of 212°F [100°C]. A gas can also be condensed by increasing the pressure. However, it must be cooled to below its critical temperature. Otherwise, no amount of pressure will cause the gas to condense. Condensation is important in the formation of rain, snow, frost, fog, and dew.
See also PRECIPITATION.   PROJECT 57

CONDENSER A condenser is any of several devices used in electrical, physical, and optical science. Each area of science uses a different kind of condenser.

An electrical condenser is a device that collects electric charge, and performs other functions in an electronic circuit. It is more commonly known as a capacitor (see CAPACITOR AND CAPACITANCE). A capacitor can block the flow of direct current but allow the flow of alternating current. It can also smooth the flow of fluctuating current (see CURRENT, ELECTRIC). Capacitors consist of two or more conductors with insulators between the two conductors (see CONDUCTION OF ELECTRICITY). Some capacitors are metal plates with glass between the

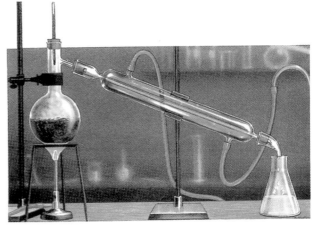

CONDENSER

A Liebig condenser consists of a long glass tube enclosed by another tube. Cold water is circulated through the outer tube. The water cools the inner tube, and vapor that passes through the inner tube condenses into a liquid.

plates. Others consist of a series of thin metal sheets separated by mica, paper, or air. Almost all electronic devices contain capacitors.

Steam condensers, also called cooling towers, are large, tanklike objects used in electric power stations. They condense live steam from steam turbines into water (see TURBINE). After the steam has been used in the operation of the turbine, it enters a chamber surrounded by tubes filled with cold water. The cold water lowers the temperature in the chamber, and the steam condenses into water. The water is then reheated to make steam again (see COOLING TOWER). Similar, but smaller, condensers are used to make distilled water, certain alcoholic beverages, and some other substances (see DISTILLATION).

An optical condenser is a device used to produce a narrow beam of intense light. It consists of two convex lenses that focus the light from a source into a bright, narrow beam. Optical condensers are used in slide projectors to shine bright light through slides and in microscopes to illuminate specimens being examined.

See also LENS; STEAM ENGINE.

CONDOR A condor is a large, flesh-eating bird that belongs to the American vulture family, Cathartidae. There are two species of condors in the world. The Andean condor lives in the Andes Mountains in South America.

The California condor used to be found in a small area of mountains in southern California. The number of California condors had steadily

CONDOR

Condors feed mainly on carrion (dead animals), but often they attack and kill weak or sick animals, including sheep. An Andean condor is pictured here.

declined to twenty-seven due to the destruction of their wilderness nesting and feeding areas and the use of chemicals in industry and agriculture. Scientists and conservationists feared that the condor would soon become extinct (see EXTINCTION).

In the early 1980s, the United States Fish and Wildlife Service began to move condor eggs and nestlings to the Los Angeles and San Diego zoos. In 1987, the few remaining wild birds were captured and placed in zoos. These efforts led to the first hatching of a condor chick bred in captivity, at the San Diego Wild Animal Park in April 1988. In 1992, a few condors were released into the wild. It is unknown how successful these efforts will be. Reintroducing birds bred in captivity is a difficult and uncertain process.

Like many other vultures, the condors eat mainly dead animals and have no feathers on their heads. The wingspan of a condor may be as great as 10 ft. [3 m]. This makes it one of the largest flying birds in the world. The condor uses its broad wings to soar high in the air while looking for food. A condor may glide for a long time without flapping its wings.

See also VULTURE.

CONDUCTION, HEAT Heat conduction is the movement of heat through a substance. For example, heat from the burner of a stove makes the underside of a pan hot. What happens is that the heat makes the atoms in the underside of the pan vibrate faster. These metal atoms are arranged in a rigid pattern called a crystal lattice. The lattice keeps its shape because of the strong forces between the atoms. However, in many metals, electrons escape from the atoms and move freely through the lattice. These electrons are called free electrons.

It is the free electrons that carry heat through good conductors, such as metals. In fact, it is because metals have free electrons that they are good conductors. The vibrating atoms of hot gas at the bottom of the pan strike nearby electrons and make them move faster. These electrons then strike other atoms inside the metal of the pan and,

ACTIVITY *Test conduction materials*

Place a metal spoon and a plastic one into a hot drink in a cup. Notice the difference in temperature of their handles after one minute. Plastic and metal conduct heat at very different rates.
Caution: Hot liquids can burn.

in turn, make them vibrate faster. In this process, the atoms themselves do not move through the pan. It is the electrons that do so, making all the atoms in the lattice vibrate faster.

Gas and liquids conduct heat differently. They do not have free electrons and are therefore not as good conductors as metals. If there is water in the pan, the rapidly vibrating atoms of the hot pan make the water molecules move about more quickly. These fast-moving molecules collide with other molecules and make them move faster. By doing so, they increase the average speed of all the molecules in the water. This increases the temperature of the water. In this way, heat is conducted from the burner through the metal of the pan to the water. It is then conducted through the water so that all the water in the pan comes to the same temperature. Convection is also important in the way heat flows through gases and liquids.

See also ATOM; CONVECTION; ELECTRON; HEAT; MOLECULE. 🔬 PROJECT 40

CONDUCTION OF ELECTRICITY

Conduction of electricity is the passage of electricity through a substance. Materials that allow the passage of electricity are called conductors. Metals are the most widely used conductors. Carbon, electrolytes (substances that transfer electric charges by the movement of ions), and gases under low pressure are also used as conductors (see IONS AND IONIZATION).

Many metals are good conductors because they contain atoms that have loosely held electrons (see ATOM; ELECTRON). These electrons are free to move within the metal. When an electric battery is connected across the ends of a metal wire, the negatively charged free electrons move away from the end connected to the negative terminal and flow toward the positive terminal. This flow of electrons is called an electric current (see CURRENT, ELECTRIC; ELECTRICITY). The more free electrons a metal has, the easier it is for electricity to move through it. Copper, aluminum, silver, and gold are the best conductors because they all have at least one free electron per atom. Most electrical wires are made of copper or aluminum.

Other materials are called poor conductors. Poor conductors resist the flow of electricity and change its energy to heat. The amount of resistance depends upon the material, its length, and its cross-sectional area. Heating units in electric stoves and toasters, for example, use the resistance principle to generate heat. Resistance to electrical flow is measured in units called ohms. A resistance of one ohm is relatively small. If a 1.5-volt battery is connected to a conductor with a resistance of one ohm, the battery causes 9,375,000,000,000,000,000 (over 9 quintillion) electrons to flow past a point in the conductor in one second. This is a relatively large current of 1.5 amperes (see AMPERE; OHM; RESISTANCE, ELECTRICAL; VOLT).

Insulators are substances that contain tightly bound electrons that cannot move from their atoms. These substances cannot easily conduct electricity. Glass, mica, and rubber are the most common insulators. Wood and plastic are also used as insulators.

Some materials, such as silicon and germanium,

are neither good conductors nor insulators. They are called semiconductors. Some materials are superconductors. That is, they have no electrical resistance. For the most part, these materials must be at extremely low temperatures in order to be superconductors. However, scientists are working to make some substances superconductors at higher temperatures (see SEMICONDUCTOR; SUPER-CONDUCTIVITY).   🔬 PROJECT 31

CONGLOMERATE (kən glŏm'ər ĭt) A conglomerate is a rock made of rounded pebbles held together by a fine-grained natural cement. Before they were joined by the cement, the pebbles became rounded by weathering and by the action of streams and oceans. The natural cement is made of sand and various substances containing calcium, silicon, or iron.

Much conglomerate material was formed during the Triassic period in North America, northwestern

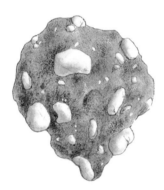

CONGLOMERATE

The fragments embedded in a conglomerate show the kind of rock that was originally broken down to rubble. The rubble was then joined by natural cement to form the conglomerate—a kind of second-generation rock. Its mixed appearance has led to the common name "pudding stone."

Europe, and New Zealand. (The Triassic period lasted from about 225 million years ago to 193 million years ago). Conglomerates are often found in areas that once experienced glaciation (see GLACIATION). The most common environment for conglomerates are alluvial fans (deposits of alluvium where a stream flows from a gorge upon a plain or where one stream flows into another stream), river channels, and beaches (see ALLUVIUM).

See also SEDIMENTARY ROCK.

CONIFER (kŏn'ə fər) A conifer is a tree or shrub that bears its seeds in cones. Conifers are usually trees, but some are shrubs. There are about four hundred species of conifers in the world. They are found mostly in temperate climates. Conifers that are common in North America include pine, fir, larch, spruce, hemlock, redwood, yew, and juniper.

Most conifers are evergreens with slender leaves called needles. Although the needles die and fall off like the leaves of deciduous trees, they do not all fall at the same time and new needles grow before the old needles fall. Because of this pattern, a conifer

CONIFER—Red fir

Red firs, seen here towering 175 ft. [53 m] above the road, are native to the western United States. The red bark that gives the trees their name develops only at high altitudes.

CONIFER—Cones

The cone of the red fir is up to 8 in. [20 cm] long and, like those of all true firs, it stands upright on the branches. Fir cones fall to pieces when they are ripe and the seeds float away on the breeze. Pine and spruce cones stay in one piece and the scales simply open up to let the seeds escape.

always has needles—hence, the name *evergreen* (see EVERGREEN).

Conifers have two kinds of cones: male and female. The female cone contains ovules. Wind blows pollen from the male cone into the female cone. This transfer of pollen is called pollination. The pollen produces sperm (male sex cells), which fertilize the eggs (female sex cells) in the ovules in the female cone. The ovules develop into seeds, which contain the new embryo plants that developed from the fertilized eggs. The seeds, which mature inside the female cone, fall to the ground to grow into new trees. Most cones release the seeds soon after the cones appear on the tree. Pine cones, however, must mature for two years. *See also* GYMNOSPERM; POLLINATION.

CONNECTIVE TISSUE

Connective tissue is the material that connects body tissues and organs, holds organs in place, and supports the body. Bones, cartilage, ligaments, and tendons are all examples of connective tissue (see BONE; CARTILAGE; LIGAMENT; TENDON).

Connective tissue has relatively few cells but has substantial material between the cells. This intercellular material contains long, white and yellow fibers. Most of the fibers are white and are made of collagen (see COLLAGEN). The yellow fibers are made of a material called elastin and are able to stretch easily.

Connective tissue other than bones and cartilage is often called connective tissue proper. Connective tissue proper can be one of two types, depending on the structure and function of the intercellular material. These two types are loose and dense connective tissue. Loose connective tissue, or areolar tissue, surrounds various organs and muscles. It is soft, filmy, delicate, and flexible, holding structures in place while allowing movement between them.

Loose connective tissue is not very resistant to stress. Reticular tissue is a specialized type of loose connective tissue that provides a framework, especially in the bone marrow, to support the cells that produce red and white blood cells.

Dense connective tissue has many more fibers than loose connective tissue. These fibers are arranged in sheets and bundles, which are less flexible and more resistant to stress than loose connective tissue. This kind of connective tissue forms tough coverings for some organs, such as the kidneys. Dense connective tissue also forms ligaments. *See also* ARTHRITIS; BLOOD; BONE MARROW.

CONSCIOUSNESS

Consciousness is the state of being awake and mentally alert. Psychologists recognize the existence of different levels or states of consciousness between wide awake and fast asleep.

Sleep is the state of consciousness in which the activity of the unconscious mind takes the form of dreaming (see DREAM; SLEEP). Hypnosis is a special state of consciousness in which the person who has been hypnotized stops thinking for himself or herself and responds, instead, to the suggestions of the hypnotist (see HYPNOSIS).

Drugs can produce changes in a person's state of consciousness. By stimulating the central nervous system, the caffeine in coffee or tea can make a person feel more awake and alert. Alcohol, on the other hand, can produce the opposite state, one of drowsiness or even unconsciousness. Some drugs, called hallucinogens, can produce a state of waking dream, or hallucination (see HALLUCINOGEN).

An important area of psychological research today is the role that consciousness plays in organizing a person's memory.

CONSERVATION

Conservation is the practice of saving things from loss or waste. If a light bulb is left on when no one is in the room, the electricity being used is wasted. If the light bulb is turned off, the electricity is being conserved. Conservation allows future generations of people to enjoy the things people enjoy today. For example, conservationists have helped pass laws to protect plants and animals that might otherwise disappear forever. These organisms are called endangered species. Conservation laws make sure that these endangered species survive (see ENDANGERED SPECIES).

The earth has many natural resources, such as water, air, soil, minerals, trees and other plants, petroleum (oil), and natural gas. People depend on these resources to live. Life would be impossible without clean water, air, and food. Modern life would be very different without petroleum and natural gas. In order to make sure that these resources do not run out, they must be conserved (see NATURAL RESOURCE).

Perhaps the most important resources to be conserved are the various sources of energy. For example, there is only a certain amount of oil in the earth. Once that is gone, there will be no more. While scientists try to discover other types of fuel to use, oil and products that are made from oil, such as gasoline, kerosene, and some plastics, must not be wasted. Automobiles are now being made that do not use as much gasoline. These new cars also do not pollute the air as much. This conserves the air. Laws also have been made to control the pollution of rivers and other bodies of water. This conserves not only the water itself, but the plant and animal life that lives in water (see POLLUTION).

Wildlife conservation is important for various reasons. Nature is very complicated. Every plant and animal plays a part. Sometimes, even scientists who study nature do not realize how important

RARE BUTTERFLIES

The large copper butterfly is one of the world's rarest butterflies. It has disappeared from many places because its wetland habitats are being drained for farming. It is now being protected on nature reserves.

some organisms are. However, it is known that if all the hawks in the world were killed, for example, mice, which hawks eat, would become so numerous that they would eat most of the food humans eat and spread diseases. To keep nature in balance, all species must continue to exist.

Beautiful, undeveloped land must also be conserved. Some areas must be left undeveloped so there are forests to walk in and beaches to stroll along. National parks conserve land as well as wildlife and other natural resources.

The field of conservation includes many different career opportunities. These include careers in energy conservation, forestry, recycling, soil conservation, waste management, water quality control, and wildlife management.

See also ECOLOGY; ECOSYSTEM; ENVIRONMENT.

RESTORATION AFTER MINING

Many conservationists oppose strip mining because of the damage it does to the environment. Coal companies are now required to restore the landscape once the coal has been removed from the strip mines. Such restoration helps reduce long-term environmental damage.

GAME RESERVES

Many of Africa's large mammals are becoming rare because they are hunted, but large game reserves have been created so that the animals can live in safety. Here a hippopotamus is being watched in a reserve in Botswana.

CONSERVATION LAWS A conservation law describes something that stays unchanged—is "conserved"—during a chemical, physical, or biological process. Such laws help scientists understand how the processes work. An example is the law of conservation of electric charge, which states that the amount of electric charge in an isolated system never changes. This is often useful in understanding the behavior of an electrical circuit, in which the changes in currents, voltages, and charge can become very complicated (see ELECTRICITY).

One of the earliest conservation laws states that the momentum in an isolated system of moving bodies stays constant. (Momentum is force of motion.) The momentum of an object is the result of multiplying its mass by its velocity (see MASS; MOMENTUM; VELOCITY). The law says, for example, that if a heavy truck smashes into a wall, the momentum of the truck before the smash is equal to its momentum afterwards, plus the momentum of all the fragments of the wall added together.

Many other conservation laws exist. They often explain why some process cannot happen. For example, a photon, or particle of light, has no electric charge. Often a high-energy photon turns into a negatively charged electron and a positively charged positron (an anti-electron). The positive and negative charges of these particles cancel out. Therefore, the total charge is still zero, which is in agreement with the law of conservation of electric charge. A result of the law is that a photon could never turn into a single electron, for example, because then negative electric charge would have been created.

See also CHEMISTRY.

CONSTELLATION A constellation is a group of stars visible in a particular area of the sky. Today, eighty-eight constellations are recognized. Most of the constellations visible from the Northern Hemisphere were observed by people of ancient civilizations, such as the Greeks and Romans. They named the constellations after characters in their mythology, such as Hercules, Cassiopeia, Andromeda, Orion, and Perseus. Other constellations

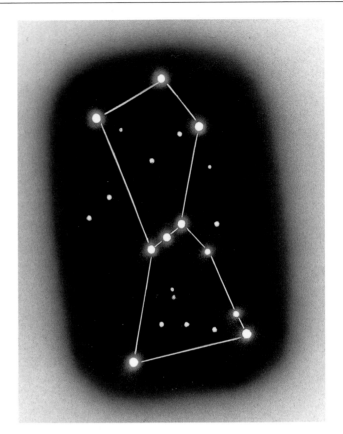

CONSTELLATION

This is the constellation of Orion, the hunter. It is a bright constellation seen in the southern winter sky of the Northern Hemisphere. The four bright stars show the hunter's knees and shoulders. Three stars in a line show his belt.

are named after animals, such as Scorpius (the scorpion), Cancer (the crab), Aries (the ram), Leo (the lion), and Taurus (the bull). The twelve constellations that lie on the ecliptic (the sun's apparent path) define the zodiac (see ZODIAC).

Most people looking at the sky today probably find it easier to pick out patterns of triangles, squares, or other familiar shapes than to see the figure of a warrior, queen, or animal. For example, the easily recognized Big Dipper is a group of stars that forms part of the constellation Ursa Major (Great Bear). The Little Dipper is part of Ursa Minor (Little Bear) (see BIG DIPPER AND LITTLE DIPPER).

Dividing the stars into constellations makes finding celestial bodies, such as certain stars or planets, easier. Ships can also be navigated using constellations as a guide (see NAVIGATION). Because the earth revolves around the sun, different constellations appear in the sky at different times of the year. Also, every day, a particular constellation appears four minutes earlier than it did the day before.

CONSTELLATIONS VISIBLE ALL YEAR

(Circumpolar constellations, lying in the northern sky.)

Ursa Minor   Ursa Major   Camelopardalis   Cassiopeia   Cepheus   Draco

SOME MAJOR CONSTELLATIONS CHANGING THROUGH THE YEAR

Season	Eastern Evening Sky	Southern Evening Sky	Western Evening Sky
Spring (April 1)	Virgo	Gemini	Orion
	Boötes	Hydra	Canis Major
	Corona Borealis	Leo	
Summer (July 1)	Lyra	Boötes	Leo
	Aquila	Corona Borealis	Virgo
	Cygnus	Scorpius	
		Sagittarius	
		Ophiuchus	
Fall (October 1)	Perseus	Lyra	Boötes
	Taurus	Aquila	Corona Borealis
		Cygnus	Ophiuchus
		Pegasus	Sagittarius
Winter (January 1)	Canis Major	Perseus	Cygnus
	Gemini	Taurus	Pegasus
	Canis Minor	Orion	
	Auriga		

This table shows the locations of some of the main constellations visible from the north temperate latitudes at 9 P.M. on four different dates each year. On other dates, the entries are applicable at slightly different times in the evening.
The column headed "Southern Evening Sky" shows constellations from the southern horizon to roughly overhead.
Some constellations close to the north celestial pole can be seen throughout the year. These circumpolar constellations are listed at the beginning of the table. From places in the southernmost United States, some of these, such as Ursa Major, are not circumpolar. From places farther north, more constellations are circumpolar.

The Greek astronomer Ptolemy named forty-eight of the eighty-eight known constellations (see PTOLEMY). Ptolemy observed the forty-eight constellations from the Northern Hemisphere. Different constellations are seen from the Southern Hemisphere. Crux—also called the Southern Cross—is a well-known constellation seen from the Southern Hemisphere.
See also HEMISPHERE.

CONSUMER In the natural world, a consumer is any living thing that eats or consumes other living things or their remains (see FOOD CHAIN; PRODUCER).

The caterpillar that munches its way through leaves is a consumer, and so is the bird that eats the caterpillar. The cat that eats the bird is also a consumer. The beetles and fly maggots that eat the cat's dead body are consumers too.

CONTINENTAL DRIFT

The continental drift theory states that the seven continents were once one supercontinent and have since moved apart to their present positions. The supercontinent, called Pangaea, formed about 250 million years ago, during the Permian period. About 50 million years later, during the Triassic period, Pangaea separated into two huge land masses: Laurasia, consisting of the present-day continents of North America and most of Eurasia, and Gondwanaland, consisting of what are now South America, Africa, India, Australia, and Antarctica. Laurasia and Gondwanaland eventually broke up to form the modern continents (see GEO-LOGICAL TIME SCALE).

Evidence of continental drift The German scientist Alfred Wegener is the father of the continental drift theory. In the early 1900s, he presented evidence to support his theory. For example, the continents bordering the Atlantic Ocean match each other like jigsaw puzzle pieces. Wegener also cited similarities between rocks, fossils, and mountain structures on opposite sides of the Atlantic.

The idea of continental drift became accepted in the 1960s. Geologists studied the magnetism of rocks. This magnetism shows the direction of the earth's magnetic field in relation to the rocks at the time the rocks were formed. The evidence showed how the rocks have moved since that time.

Ocean research in the past thirty years shows that the continents fit together even better than Wegener thought. This is because of the continental shelf, an underwater extension of the coastline. The continental shelf is the true edge of the continents. By mapping it, scientists have found that the continents match almost perfectly (see CONTINENTAL SHELF).

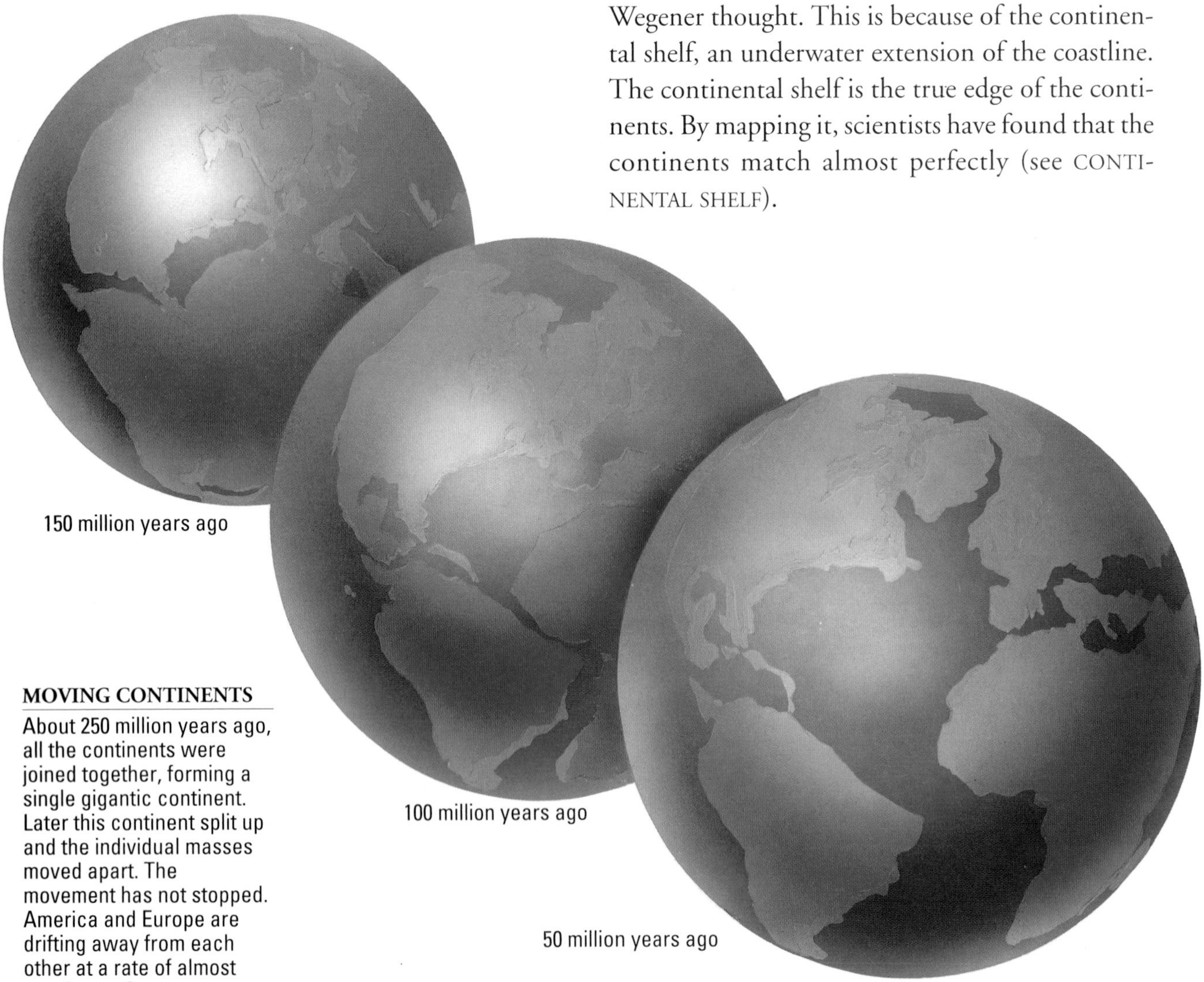

150 million years ago

100 million years ago

50 million years ago

MOVING CONTINENTS
About 250 million years ago, all the continents were joined together, forming a single gigantic continent. Later this continent split up and the individual masses moved apart. The movement has not stopped. America and Europe are drifting away from each other at a rate of almost 1 in. [2.5 cm] a year.

New evidence supporting the continental drift theory has been found by studying fossils. Paleontologists, who study fossils, have found fossils of extinct plants and reptiles in Antarctica. Thus, they believe that Antarctica was a warm continent before it drifted to its present position around the South Pole (see PALEONTOLOGY).

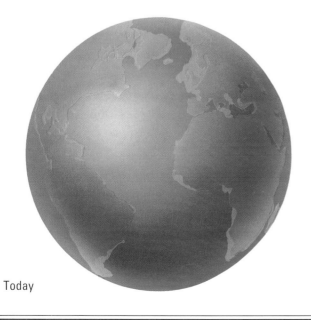

Today

VOLCANOES

The continents move because of a process called "plate tectonics." Each continent is embedded in one of the plates that form the surface of the earth. The plates are continually growing along one edge and being destroyed along another. Volcanoes are found at the growing edges.

Cause of continental drift Scientists think that the earth's crust consists of several rigid plates (see PLATE TECTONICS). These plates form the ocean bed and lie underneath the continents. The movement of the plates is responsible for continental drift and also causes earthquakes. When two plates collide, one is forced beneath the other. Where the collision occurs at the edge of a continent, a volcanic mountain range is created (see VOLCANO). For example, India, after breaking away from Gondwanaland, drifted north until it hit the Asian mainland. This collision is thought to have caused the Himalayas to form (see MOUNTAIN). California is subject to earthquakes because of the San Andreas fault, which forms the edge between two plates that are grinding past one another. *See also* EARTHQUAKE; FAULT; GEOPHYSICS.

CONTINENTAL SHELF The continental shelf is an underwater extension of a continent. It slopes gradually from the coastline until it reaches the continental edge. At the continental edge, the continental slope begins. The steep continental slope plunges to the ocean floor.

The continental shelf waters are fairly shallow, usually less than 660 ft. [200 m] deep. These waters are the best fishing areas of the oceans.

The continental shelf varies in width. Off the country of Chile in South America, for example, there is no shelf, so the seabed plunges steeply to the ocean floor. In other places, such as the British Isles, the continental shelf is quite wide.

See also CONTINENTAL DRIFT; OCEANOGRAPHY.

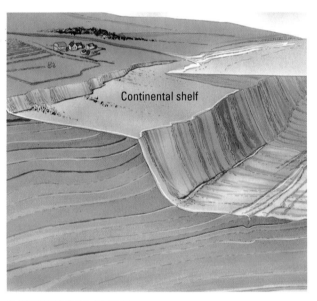

CONTINENTAL SHELF
The continental shelf is the edge of the continent that is underwater. Beyond the continental edge, the ocean floor slopes steeply away, forming the continental slope, and levels off as it reaches the deep ocean.

CONTOUR LINE A contour line is one kind of isoline. Isolines are lines on a map that show some characteristic, such as temperature or elevation (height above sea level), that is the same throughout an area. When isolines show elevation, they are called contour lines. On a map with contour lines, all the places with the same elevation are connected by a line. The contour lines give an idea of the general shape of the landforms being shown on the map. Isobaths are contour lines drawn in

blue to show ocean depth. Isotherms are isolines showing temperature, and isobars are lines showing barometric pressure (see ISOBAR AND ISOTHERM). *See also* MAP AND MAPPING.

CONTOUR LINE
If a landscape were flooded to different depths, e.g., 165 ft. [50 m], 330 ft. [100 m], and so on, the tidemarks left around the hills and valleys would represent the contour lines. In actual practice such lines that join points at the same height above sea level are established on maps by surveying.

CONTRACEPTION (kŏn′trə sĕp′shən) Contraception, also known as birth control, involves preventing conception or impregnation. Conception is the fertilization of an egg by a sperm. Impregnation occurs when the fertilized egg becomes attached to the wall of the uterus, and a new life starts to develop (see PREGNANCY).

Different methods of contraception are in use today. Barrier methods, such as condoms, contraceptive sponges, and diaphragms, prevent the sperm and egg from meeting. Condoms are the only contraceptives that also prevent transmission of disease. Barrier methods also may use chemicals to kill sperm. Hormonal pills prevent the female from producing a mature egg. Intrauterine devices (IUDs) prevent the implantation of a fertilized egg in the uterus. Natural family planning includes the rhythm method, in which sexual intercourse is avoided during the period each month when the egg is released into the reproductive tract. Surgery to sterilize either the male or the female is another form of contraception.

See also REPRODUCTION.

CONTROL TECHNOLOGY Control technology is used to regulate machines automatically. There are two types of control technology systems: open-loop and closed-loop. An open-loop control system follows a preset series of instructions. A washing machine is an example of an open-loop control system because it carries out a preprogrammed series of operations. A closed-loop control system uses feedback to regulate a machine automatically. The term *feedback* is used because a small part of the machine's output is fed back to the input to keep the machine operating within preset limits. The central heating system of a house is an example of a closed-loop. Information about heat produced by the system is fed back into the system to control its operation. It operates a thermostat that switches the heating system on and off to maintain a stable temperature. A thermostat is an example of a control device. Other control devices include sensors that respond to changes in rate of flow, liquid level, temperature, or pressure. Signals from these and other control devices then command the system to adjust for the changes they sense.
See also COMMUNICATION; THERMOSTAT.

CONVECTION Convection is one way in which heat moves from one place to another. It happens in gases and liquids. For example, a heater warms the air around it. As air becomes hot, it expands. This means its density is reduced, so it rises. As it rises, it is replaced by cooler air. Then the cooler air near the heater also gets warm and rises. This movement of heated air away from a hot object, along with the flow of cooler air toward the hot object, is called a convection current. In this way, warm air is moved to all parts of a room.

CONVECTION

Gliders and soaring birds gain height by using convection currents in the atmosphere called thermals. They travel by gliding from one thermal to another, regaining height in each thermal.

Convection can also take place in liquids. For example, convection occurs in a pan of cold water on a hot stove. As the water near the bottom of the pan warms up, it expands and becomes lighter. The cold water near the top of the pan sinks, and the heated water rises to the top. In this way, a constant circulation of the liquid occurs, taking heat from the bottom of the liquid to the top. Eventually, the heat is spread throughout the liquid. The circulating water is a convection current. The convection current goes on until all the water has the same temperature.

Convection is important in meteorology (the study of the atmosphere and the weather). Winds are caused when hot air rises in warm regions and cooler air rushes in to replace hot air. Convection is also important to glider pilots, who try to find convection currents in the air to carry them to higher altitudes.

See also CONDUCTION, HEAT.  PROJECT 40

CONVEX The term *convex* refers to a surface that curves outward at the center. For example, a convex lens is thicker in the middle than at the edges. A magnifying glass is an example of a convex lens.
See also CONCAVE; LENS.

CONVEX

A convex lens, above, has a surface that curves, or bulges, outward at the center.

CONVEYOR A conveyor is a machine that is used to move many objects, or people, from one place to another. The most common form of conveyor is the conveyor belt.

Conveyor belts play an important role in mass production in factories. Automobiles, and many other complicated products, move along an assembly line on a conveyor belt system. Workers stand in one place, and the products to be worked on move past them. Conveyor belts are used at airports to carry luggage from ticket counters to the baggage rooms. Moving sidewalks, which are large, flat conveyor belts, are used to speed up the flow of people on foot in some buildings and transportation centers, including airports. Escalators, which are moving stairs that carry people between floors in buildings, are another form of conveyor belt. Conveyor belts are also used in mining operations and in ship and train terminals.

A conveyor belt consists of an endless belt that is looped over two pulleys. One of the pulleys is called the drive pulley. It is attached to an electric motor. The drive pulley rotates and causes the belt to move. The belt, which is usually thick rubber or leather, travels over a series of rollers that support it and reduce friction (see FRICTION). The objects or materials are carried along on the belt at a moderate speed in a straight line. Conveyor belts can carry materials up steeper grades, or slopes, better than trucks or railroad trains can. In fact, the steepness of the grade is limited only by the slope at which the material will slide back down the belt. Some belts have a series of raised barriers that prevent objects from rolling back down a slope.

Some conveyor belts are flat, and objects are simply placed on them to be carried away. Bulk

CONVEYOR
Airline passengers collect their luggage from a conveyor belt in an airport terminal. The luggage conveyor belt is an endless loop so that suitcases are carried around again and again until they are collected.

materials, such as wheat and sugar, are carried in belts that are curved to form a trough. This prevents the material from spilling as the belt moves. Other types of factory conveyors consist of endless chains with buckets hanging from the chains at short intervals. Liquid materials are carried in the buckets. Another type of chain conveyor has a series of hooks at short intervals. Objects are hung on the hooks and carried along.

CONVULSION A convulsion is a sudden, uncontrolled, jerking muscular movement. Convulsions also are known as seizures or spasms. When someone has a convulsion, the voluntary muscles in the body, such as those in the face, arms, legs, and back, contract and relax in a violent way. Even though these muscles are normally under his or her control, a person has no control over the convulsive action.

Convulsions are symptoms of some disorders. A common disorder that involves convulsions is epilepsy. Convulsions can also be caused by fever in children, injury, poison, brain tumors, rabies, and many other disorders (see EPILEPSY; RABIES).

Convulsions should be treated properly and immediately. The person should be kept warm, quiet, and relaxed. He or she should be taken to a hospital emergency room, or an ambulance should be called. First aid includes preventing injury from falling, from biting the tongue or cheek, and from striking hard objects during convulsions.

COOLING TOWER A cooling tower is a structure often used in industry for cooling large amounts of hot water. In industry, a great deal of water is used to cool things. For example, water is used to cool engines. When water is used this way, it becomes very hot. The water must then be cooled before it can be returned to the cooling system or run into rivers or other bodies of water.

A cooling tower is a device for exposing the maximum surface area of the water to the air. In this way, the water loses its heat to the surrounding air more quickly. The water is pumped to the top of a tower. Then it is allowed to fall on a series of devices called baffles. The baffles cause the water to break

COOLING TOWER

The tall, wide shape of a power station cooling tower is carefully chosen to create a flow of air upward through the tower. The air-flow cools hot water from the power station's cooling system so that it can be returned to the power station and used again.

up into thin films and drops. In this condition, water is able to release its heat to the air quite rapidly.

There are two main kinds of cooling towers. The open tower, or atmospheric tower, is of louvered construction, which means that there are slits along the walls and roof. Air is circulated through the side walls. A chimney cooling tower is often more than 200 ft. [61 m] in height and much wider than an open tower. A chimney cooling tower can cool large amounts of water very quickly. In towers of this type, air enters at the bottom and is drawn upward by a draft. The draft is due to the higher temperature of the water inside the tower. Chimney cooling towers are commonly used in large industrial organizations, such as power plants. Most often, the towers are made of concrete. *See also* CONDENSER.

COORDINATES When a cross is made by drawing two lines at right angles to each other, it sets off four areas called quadrants. Any point in a quadrant can be represented by two coordinates (also called rectangular Cartesian coordinates). The horizontal line is referred to as the *x*-axis and the vertical line as the *y*-axis. Each axis is subdivided into units.

In the top part of the diagram, the red point is three units along the *x*-axis and two units along the *y*-axis. The coordinates of the point are written (3, 2). The *x* coordinate is always written first. The point where the two axes cross is called the origin and is represented as (0, 0).

Negative numbers are used to represent units to the left of the origin on the *x*-axis and below the origin on the *y*-axis. Therefore, any points in the lower left quadrant have two negative coordinates.

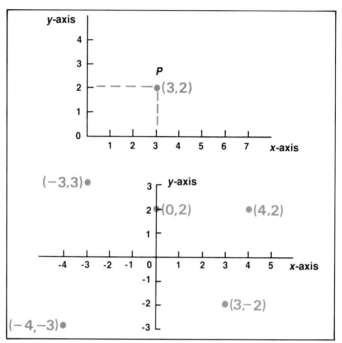

COORDINATES

The point in the upper diagram has the coordinates (3,2). The lower diagram shows how negative coordinates are also possible. These are called rectangular Cartesian coordinates because there are two axes at right angles defining position. Three or more axes can be used to give coordinates in advanced math and algebra.

COORDINATION Coordination is the efficient linking of activities in various parts of the body so that the whole animal works properly. When running, for example, an animal has to move its legs in the right way and at just the right time to avoid tripping itself. When you want to pick something up, you have to coordinate the movements of your body so that your hand goes to just the right place. Acting on signals from your eyes, your brain "tells" your hand where to go. You can experiment with coordination by balancing a stick on your hand. Your eyes will tell you which way the stick is swaying. Your brain will coordinate your movements so that you can keep the stick upright. Try this experiment with your eyes closed, and the stick will quickly fall.

Coordination also means the efficient working of a group of animals, such as a group of lions on a hunting trip. If the individual lions do not work together, they are unlikely to catch much food.

COOT The coot is a duck-sized water bird that belongs to the rail family (Rallidae). Of the world's ten species of coots, the American coot is the only one found in North America. It is 12 in. [30 cm] long and has a wingspan of 25 in. [62.5 cm]. The American coot is gray with a black head, lobed (scalloped) toes, and a thick, short, whitish bill. It is found along the shores of fresh water and salt water. Coots feed on plants and invertebrates (animals without backbones) that they find on shore, on the water's surface, and underwater.

COOT
There are ten species of coots in the world.

COPERNICUS (kō pûr′nə kəs) (1473–1543) Nicolaus Copernicus was a Polish astronomer. He is often called the father of modern astronomy. Copernicus was born in Torun, Poland. He studied medicine and theology (religious thought) at the University of Krakow. He later studied astronomy in Italy.

Before his time, most people thought that the

COPERNICUS
Copernicus put forward the theory that the universe is heliocentric—meaning with the sun at the center. This chart, dating from 1708, shows the sun at the center with the orbits of Mercury, Venus, Earth (with the moon), Mars, Saturn, and Jupiter. The figure at the bottom right of the picture is supposed to be Copernicus.

sun, stars, and planets revolved around a stationary (unmoving) Earth. Copernicus, however, developed the theory that the sun, not the earth, was the center of the solar system.

In his book *Concerning the Revolutions of Celestial Spheres,* Copernicus reasoned that the sun, stars, and other heavenly bodies only seemed to move around the earth each day because the earth itself was revolving.

This shocked many people because it required a change in their whole conception of the universe. It was difficult for them to accept that the earth was a planet like any other planet and was not the center of all creation. This change of thinking is called the "Copernican Revolution."
See also ASTRONOMY; SOLAR SYSTEM.

COPPER Copper (Cu) is a reddish orange metal that has been widely used for more than five thousand years. In ancient times, the chief source of copper for the people who lived around the Mediterranean Sea was the island of Cyprus. The metal therefore became known as Cyprian metal. The word *copper* comes from the Latin word *cuprum,* which was the Romans' name for "Cyprian metal."

Most copper is found in about seven types of ores. Copper ores usually contain less than 4 percent copper. These ores may contain other metals as well, such as zinc, gold, lead, and nickel. The main copper ores are sulfides (compounds of metals with sulfur). They include bornite, copper pyrites, and chalcocite. Chalcocite is commonly called copper glance. Oxide ores (compounds of metals with oxygen), such as cuprite and malachite, also contain valuable amounts of copper. Native copper, which is almost pure copper, occurs very rarely in nature.

About 8 million metric tons [7.8 million tons] of copper are mined each year. Much of the world's copper comes from the mountains of Canada, the United States, and South America. Zambia and Russia also produce much copper.

Copper can be obtained from ores in many different ways. The way that copper is obtained from copper pyrites (sulfides of iron and copper) is one basic method. Copper pyrites is crushed and smelted (heated) to produce copper matte. Copper matte contains from 25 to 50 percent copper. The matte is heated, and air is blown through to oxidize the sulfur present. The iron is removed as slag (waste), leaving fairly pure copper.

Another common ore is cuprite. This oxide ore is smelted with coal or coke to remove oxygen and produce copper metal (see COKE). Cuprite may also be treated with chemicals that dissolve the copper in the ore. Copper metal is then precipitated from the solution (see PRECIPITATE).

These methods give almost pure copper. This copper may then be refined by electrolysis (see ELECTROLYSIS).

The physical properties of copper make it valuable to industry. One of the useful properties of copper is its conductivity. Copper is best known for its ability to conduct electricity. Silver is a better conductor, but far too expensive for common use. Copper alloys (mixtures of metals) do not conduct electricity nearly as well as pure copper. Impurities in refined copper greatly reduce conductivity. For example, 0.05 percent arsenic lessens the conductivity of copper by 15 percent (see CONDUCTION OF ELECTRICITY). Copper is also a good conductor of heat. This property makes copper useful in cooking utensils, radiators, and refrigerators (see CONDUCTION, HEAT).

Another useful property of copper is that the metal is malleable, or easy to shape. Copper does not crack under many difficult conditions. It can be shaped when it is either hot or cold. Copper can be drawn into thin wires. Copper can be rolled into sheets less than 0.002 in. [0.05 mm] thick.

In damp air, copper turns from a reddish orange to a reddish brown color. However, after long exposure to damp air, copper becomes coated with a green film called patina. Patina protects copper against further corrosion (see CORROSION).

With so many different properties, copper has thousands of uses, ranging from rain gutters to electronic systems for rockets. Because copper is the best low-cost conductor of electricity, the electrical industry uses about 60 percent of the copper produced. Large amounts of copper wire are used in telephone systems, television sets, motors, and many other kinds of electrical equipment.

Copper is used to make many alloys, such as brass and bronze (see BRASS; BRONZE). Copper alloys are made into thousands of useful objects, from

COPPER

Native copper—copper metal not combined with other elements—is rare in nature. It is found as small, spiky masses.

lighting fixtures, plumbing fixtures, door-knobs, and clocks to mailboxes, pans, jewelry, and coins.

Copper compounds help improve soil and destroy harmful insects. In paints, copper compounds help protect materials against corrosion. Also, copper in very small amounts is vital to all plant and animal life. The chemical element has an atomic number of 29. Its relative atomic mass is 63.55. Copper melts at 1,981°F [1,083°C] and boils at 4,652°F [2,567°C].

See also ELEMENT.

COPPERHEAD

The copperhead is a poisonous snake belonging to the viper family (see PIT VIPER). It can grow up to 4 ft. [1.2 m] long, but most copperheads measure about 2.5 ft. [76 cm] in length.

The copperhead has a brown and copper red body arranged in a pattern that resembles hourglasses placed side by side. It lives in the eastern United States and can be found as far west as Texas and Kansas.

The copperhead eats mostly rodents and other small animals, such as frogs. It finds its warm-blooded prey by using the temperature receptors located in the deep pits halfway between its eyes and nostrils, and it can do this in total darkness. The venom (poison) of the copperhead, like that of its close relatives the rattlesnake and cottonmouth (water moccasin), causes internal bleeding in its victims. The copperhead usually has between three and seven live young in August or September.

COPPER SULFATE

Copper sulfate ($CuSO_4$) is a salt formed by treating copper oxide (CuO) with sulfuric acid (H_2SO_4). Known commercially as blue vitriol, copper sulfate forms as large, bright blue crystals containing molecules of water. The water-free salt is white and obtained by heating the blue crystal form to 300°F [150°C].

Copper sulfate is used mainly in agriculture as a pesticide (pest killer), feed additive, and fertilizer (substance that adds nutrients to soil). It is also used in the manufacture of other copper compounds (substances made of two or more elements), in dyeing, in batteries, and as a preservative for leather and wood. In addition, copper sulfate is used to kill algae that foul water tanks. The compound is also used in medicine to kill certain types of fungi and bacteria, and in treating certain kinds of poisoning.

See also COPPER.

CORAL

Coral is a sea animal that belongs to the class Anthozoa of the phylum Cnidaria (see CNIDARIA). Corals are small, invertebrate organisms with short tentacles (see INVERTEBRATE). Corals make and live in hard, stony cups. Because most corals live in large colonies made up of millions of individual animals, these hard cups grow together and form mounds. When a coral dies, the cup in which it once lived remains. New coral grows on top of it, causing the mound to become larger. Very

CORAL

Coral colonies grow in an amazing variety of shapes, many of them branched like colorful plants. Here, you see several different kinds of corals growing together on a coral reef. The large one in the middle is called a brain coral because its surface looks like a human brain.

large reefs (narrow ridges at or near the water surface) are formed in this way, but they can grow only in clear, warm seas. The largest coral reef in the world is the Great Barrier Reef off the coast of Australia. The Great Barrier Reef is 1,250 mi. [2,010 km] long.

Coral reefs can be dangerous to ships, which may hit them and sink. However, coral reefs offer protection and food to many other plants and animals. Large numbers of fishes and invertebrates live among coral reefs. The South Pacific Ocean is famous for its coral reefs. Coral may be found as fossils in some inland parts of the United States. It grew there when the ocean once covered much of the land.

See also ATOLL; LIMESTONE.

CORAL SNAKE
The coral snake is a poisonous snake that belongs to the family Elapidae. It is related to the cobra (see COBRA). Only two species of coral snake live in the United States. The larger of the two reaches about 42 in. [105 cm] in length. Both have a small, blunt head and a body ringed with yellow, red, and black bands. The red bands always touch the yellow ones. Several harmless snakes have similar colors, but the red does not touch the yellow. Other species of coral snakes, with various patterns, live in Central and South America.

Coral snakes have a venom (poison) that affects the nervous system of any animal that is bitten by the snake. The snake does not squirt the venom but must chew on the victim to mix the venom with the victim's blood. Frogs, lizards, and other snakes are the main food of the coral snake.

CORAL SNAKE
This is the eastern coral snake. It lives in the southeastern United States.

CORE
The central part of the earth is called its core. The diameter of the core is 4,200 mi. [7,000 km], slightly more than half of the earth's diameter. The outer edge of the core is liquid and its temperature is approximately 7,600°F [4,200°C]. At the center of the core the temperature is not much greater, about 8,500°F [4,700°C]. The pressure at the center from the overlying rock and metal of the earth is so great that the core material is squeezed into the solid state (see LIQUID; SOLID).

The core consists mostly of iron, mixed with smaller amounts of nickel and other elements. When the earth was first formed 4.6 billion years ago, it was heated up by energy released from the bombardment of meteoric material (see METEOR) left over from the formation of the planets, and by its own radioactive elements (see RADIOACTIVITY). Because of its high temperature, the material of the young earth was soft. Materials that were more dense (having more mass per unit volume) sank toward the center. So the iron in the earth settled inward to form the core. Today the core's heat is maintained by radioactive heating.

The liquid metal of the outer core is a good conductor of electricity. The rotation of the earth sets up circulation in this liquid outer core. The circulation generates electric currents. These currents produce the earth's magnetic field (see COMPASS; MAGNETISM).

Outside the core lies the solid rock of the mantle, which is 1,800 mi. [2,900 km] thick. Above the mantle lies the rock of the earth's crust, which makes up the continents and the ocean floor. It is impossible to drill to the core because the distance from the surface is far too great. But geologists have learned a great deal about the core from its effect on earthquake waves. The two types of earthquake waves that travel through the interior of the planet are called P (pressure) waves and S (shear) waves. The P waves can travel through liquid, but the S waves cannot. Because P waves can travel through the core, but S waves cannot, earth scientists discovered that the core must be liquid.

See also CRUST; EARTHQUAKE; MANTLE; PLANETS; SEISMOLOGY.

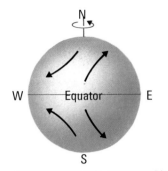

CORIOLIS EFFECT The Coriolis (kōr′ē ō′-lĭs) effect is the effect of the earth's rotation on the motion of anything traveling across it. The Coriolis effect was first described by the French physicist Gaspard de Coriolis in the 1830s. Engineers take the Coriolis effect into account when planning the flight path of a missile or rocket.

The movement of wind currents from the poles and the equator shows the Coriolis effect. The winds try to move in a straight line. However, the earth's rotation causes them to be deflected. Winds blowing toward the equator curve to the west. Winds blowing away from the equator curve to the east. The Coriolis effect also influences the direction of ocean currents.

This influence can affect the climate of a region by bringing cold or warm water to its shores. The Gulf Stream in the Atlantic Ocean is an example. It starts by flowing north from the Caribbean Sea but then curves eastward toward Europe, thus warming the southern coast of England.

CORK Cork is the lightweight, spongy material found in tree bark (see BARK). It is waterproof and resistant to many harmful chemicals. Cork cells are dead, air-filled cells with thick, waxy walls. Most commercially used cork comes from the cork oak tree, an evergreen member of the beech family. The cork oak comes from the Mediterranean countries, especially Portugal, which produces over half the world's cork, but is also cultivated in India and the western United States. It may grow as tall as 60 ft. [18 m] and live to be four hundred years old.

Once the cork oak is about twenty years old, it is ready to be stripped of its cork. The cork is removed in wide strips about 1 in. [2.5 cm] thick. It is then boiled and flattened for export. The cork-producing tissue, the cork cambium, replaces the cork within eight to ten years, when the tree is stripped again (see CAMBIUM).

Cork was used as early as 600 B.C. by the Romans for sandals and for floats for fishing nets. It is now used mainly for insulation, soundproofing, and bottle stoppers. A cork paste is used to make linoleum for floors. Cork is also still widely used for shoe soles and floats.

CORMORANT (kôr′mər ənt) A cormorant is a fish-eating bird that belongs to the family Phalacrocoracidae. Cormorants have webbed feet, long necks, and slender, hooked bills. They are excellent underwater swimmers. Cormorants are able to stay underwater for a long time while catching fish. Six species of cormorants are found in North America. They are found along the Pacific, Atlantic, and Gulf coasts.

CORMORANT
After diving, cormorants often stand with their wings stretched out for a while. This helps them to get dry.

CORN Corn is an annual plant belonging to the grass family and is the most important cereal crop in the United States. Although cultivated in temperate areas throughout the world, corn is native to North America, and now covers about 84 million acres [37.5 million hectares] of the United States. More than 50 percent of the world's corn is grown in the United States (see ANNUAL PLANT; CEREAL CROP; GRASS).

The corn plant grows as tall as 16.5 ft. [5 m] and usually has prop roots for extra support (see ROOT).

CORN

This well-filled corncob, with the remains of the silks at the top, shows how the kernels are arranged in neat rows. The enlarged single kernel beside it has been cut open to show the embryo at the bottom. Most of the kernel consists of the endosperm, which is a food supply rich in starch and oil.

Corn has both male and female flowers on the same plant. The male flowers form at the top of the stem in long spikes called tassels. The female flowers are the young ears, which grow lower down on the stem. Each ear is enclosed by a protective husk made of long, thin leaves. The ear consists of a corncob with an even number of rows of kernels. The kernels are the seeds of the corn plant. A thin, threadlike stigma runs from each kernel to the end of and out of the husk. These threads are called corn silk. Pollen from the stamens of the tassels sticks to the corn silk in pollination. A corn plant can pollinate itself or can pollinate another plant. Once pollination has taken place, the kernels begin to develop. Each kernel is made up of an embryo with an endosperm, surrounded by a protective hull (see POLLINATION).

About 65 percent of the corn grown in the United States is fed to livestock. The rest of the corn is used for human food and other products. Americans eat an average of 44 lb. [20 kg] of corn per person per year. Corn can be cooked in many ways or can be processed into cornmeal, corn oil, cornstarch, popcorn, or corn syrup. Corn syrup is the most widely used sweetener in the United States. It is added to a variety of food and cosmetic products, from juice and soft drinks to mouthwash and toothpaste. Other uses for corn and parts of the corn plant include corncob pipes, insulation, fuel, adhesives, and alcohol.

Most of the corn grown in the United States is hybrid. It has been specially bred to give it a greater resistance to disease and pests. Hybrids are stronger and produce more corn per plant. Some hybrids have been bred that are easier to harvest by machine (see BREEDING; HYBRID).

Native Americans grew corn for centuries before the first European settlers arrived in America. Corn was one of the most important food crops and was an important part of the Native Americans' religious ceremonies. Early colonists used corn for money as well as for food. Remains found in Mexico indicate that corn has existed for at least sixty thousand years.

CORONA The corona is the low density outer atmosphere of the sun or any other star. The sun's corona varies in size and can extend millions of miles into space. Its temperature averages about 4,000,000°F [2,200,000°C]. Holes in the corona allow the solar wind to constantly flow toward the earth (see SOLAR WIND). The outer part of the corona can be seen as an irregular, glowing halo that is only visible during a solar eclipse. In a solar eclipse, the surface of the sun is hidden from Earth's view by the moon.

See also ECLIPSE; STAR; SUN.

CORONA

The glowing haze of the sun's corona streams out from behind the dark disk of the moon during a solar eclipse. Normally the sun's glare is too intense to allow us to see the corona.

CORROSION Corrosion is the chemical process by which substances, especially metals, waste away. Corrosion is often the cause of great waste and expense. Also, structures such as bridges, when corroded, can be dangerously weakened. There are four main groups of chemical agents that cause corrosion: oxygen and oxidizing chemicals, acids, salts, and bases (see ACID; BASE; OXIDATION AND REDUCTION; SALT).

A common example of corrosion is the rusting of iron. This takes place in damp air. Iron is attacked by oxygen in the air. The surface of iron is changed to an iron oxide. However, corrosion from the air is not caused only by oxygen. Pollutants such as ozone and nitrogen oxides are powerful oxidizers.

In addition, many chemicals that pollute the air unite with water to form acids. Acids rapidly corrode many metals and building stones. The polluting chemicals come from fuels burned in vehicles and factories (see ACID RAIN; POLLUTION). Materials in things such as boats and ships are corroded by the salt in seawater.

CORROSION

Rusting is one of the most common types of corrosion. Rust is produced when water and air react chemically with iron or steel.

Several metals that are resistant to corrosion by acids are easily corroded by bases. The bases that pollute the atmosphere are usually products of industrial processes.

The most common way to protect a metal from corrosion is to coat the metal with materials, such as paint and varnish, that keep the attacking substances out. Sometimes efforts are made to remove the attacking substances from the environment to which the materials are exposed. Corrosion can also be prevented by plating the metal with another metal that is self-protecting or with one that draws the corrosive attack on itself (see GALVANIZING).

Some metals, such as aluminum, nickel, and chromium, grow their own protective coats. Exposed to the air, they begin to corrode, forming oxides on their surfaces. However, the oxides are in the form of hard and durable films that stay in place and do not flake away. Also, they do not let the air through to the metal underneath, so that corrosion stops. The noble metals, such as gold and platinum, are not oxidized by damp air (see NOBLE METAL).
See also RUST.

CORTEX The cortex is a ring of cells in the roots and stems of vascular plants. It is located between the epidermis (the outermost layer of cells) and the vascular tissues that carry food and water around the plant, and it varies a great deal in thickness. There are usually air spaces in it, to allow oxygen to reach the inner regions, and the outer cells of the stem cortex usually contain chlorophyll (see CHLOROPHYLL; VASCULAR PLANT).

In animal and human anatomy, *cortex* refers to the outermost part of a certain structure, such as the brain.
See also ADRENAL GLANDS; BRAIN; KIDNEY.

CORUNDUM (kə rŭn′dəm) Corundum, chemically known as aluminum oxide (Al_2O_3), is the second hardest pure mineral. Only diamond is harder. Corundum is found in metamorphic and igneous rock and in sediments (see MINERAL; ROCK).

Some transparent corundums are used as gemstones. Gemstone corundums come mainly from India, Africa, and Russia. They include ruby, sapphire, Oriental amethyst, Oriental emerald, and Oriental topaz. The colors of the gemstones are caused by impurities in the corundum. For example, the blue of sapphire is caused by iron and titanium, and the red of ruby by chromium.

Nontransparent corundum, mined chiefly in Turkey and Greece, is used as an abrasive for polishing and grinding various materials. Emery, a common abrasive, is a dark mixture of corundum, magnetite, and hematite.

See also ABRASIVE; HARDNESS.

CORUNDUM

Being one of the hardest of minerals, corundum is widely used as an abrasive. Tough paper or cloth is coated with fine corundum particles mixed with particles of iron ore to make emery paper, or emery cloth, and is used for polishing.

COSMIC RAYS Cosmic rays are streams of tiny particles that constantly enter the earth's atmosphere from outer space. They consist mainly of nuclei of atoms, especially those of hydrogen atoms (see ATOM). Cosmic rays often travel at the speed of light, which is 186,282 mi. [299,792 km] per second.

The existence of cosmic rays was proven in 1912 by Victor Franz Hess, an Austrian physicist. Hess sent gas-filled chambers aloft in a balloon. He found that the higher they went, the more ionized the gas became (see IONS AND IONIZATION). He decided that the ionization must be caused by a form of penetrating radiation that was coming from outer space.

There are two main types of cosmic rays: primary rays and secondary rays. Primary rays originate in outer space. Some are produced by solar flares and similar disturbances on other stars (see SUN). Most primary rays are thought to result from the explosion of stars called supernovas (see SUPERNOVA). Because of their electric charge, the particles in most primary rays are deflected (turned aside) by the earth's magnetic field and so are kept from entering the earth's atmosphere. The small number that do penetrate the atmosphere often collide with the nuclei of atoms in the air. This collision produces secondary cosmic rays. These make up most of the cosmic rays that reach the earth's surface.

See also RADIATION.

COSMOLOGY Cosmology is the study of the nature, size, origin, and evolution of the universe. Although astronomers have not determined the exact size of the universe, they have detected objects as far away as 10 billion light-years. A light-year is the distance light travels in one year, about 6 trillion miles [9.5 trillion kilometers]. In the observable universe, there are an estimated 1 billion galaxies, each containing an average of 100 billion stars (see GALAXY).

The universe seems to be expanding and the galaxies all moving away from each other. The big bang theory of how the universe was formed was proposed to explain this expansion. According to this theory, the universe began with a gigantic explosion between 7 and 20 billion years ago, when all matter and energy were created in an instant. The extremely high density of the newly created particles and radiation would have caused them to expand rapidly. As they expanded, they cooled and after about three minutes had formed atomic nuclei, mostly of hydrogen and helium. Over millions of years this matter condensed into stars and galaxies (see BIG BANG THEORY). The steady state theory suggests that there never was a big bang and that the universe has always been made up of a constant number of galaxies and that it always will be. Individual galaxies fade out as their stars die, but new galaxies are formed to replace them. This theory is not supported by modern astronomers. The branch of cosmology dealing with the nature and history of the heavenly bodies is called cosmogony.

See also UNIVERSE.

COTTON

The cotton plant produces fibers that provide the most common material used in clothing. Cotton clothes were used as early as 6000 B.C. by the Aztec Indians in Mexico. Ancient Greeks and Romans described cotton as "the fleece of tiny lambs growing on trees." It was not until the eighteenth century, however, that cotton came into common use. In 1793, the cotton gin was invented by Eli Whitney (see WHITNEY, ELI). The cotton gin is a machine that removes the cottonseed from the fibers. This made the production of cotton much less expensive. Today, most of the planting and harvesting is done by machines, and cotton has become a multibillion dollar industry involving more than five million Americans.

There are about twenty species of cotton plants, but only four are cultivated. Of these, upland cotton accounts for 90 percent of the cotton produced in the world. The United States ranks third in cotton production behind Russia and China. Cotton is grown throughout the world in tropical and subtropical regions.

Cotton plants are shrubs from the mallow family. They may grow 3.3 to 6.6 ft. [1 to 2 m] tall. They have long tap roots and broad, lobed leaves (see ROOT). The cotton flowers are white and live for only one day. Before they die, however, they change color from white to pink to blue to purple. During this time, the flowers pollinate themselves (see POLLINATION).

When the flower dies, the fruit, or boll, develops. It takes about two months for the cotton boll to mature into a round, green structure measuring about 2 in. [5 cm] in diameter. Inside the boll are many small seeds and the cotton fibers. The fibers are about 1.25 in. [3 cm] long and are 90 percent cellulose (see CELLULOSE). Their function is to help to scatter the seeds, but the farmers harvest the bolls before the fibers can be blown away.

The cotton plant has many important uses. Each person in the United States uses an average of 20 lb. [9 kg] of cotton and cotton products every year. The cotton fiber is used in textiles for clothes, rugs, sheets, bandages, and bookbindings. The cottonseed can be squeezed for an oil used in margarine, salad oil, and an ice-cream-like dessert called mellorine. Less than 10 percent of the cottonseed oil is used for nonfood products, such as soap. Cotton meal is the solid left after the oil has been removed from the seed. This meal is often used for livestock feed or is processed into a flour for human use. As well as the long fibers, the

DEFOLIANT

Mature cotton plants are sprayed with defoliant chemicals to remove the leaves before the harvesting machines move in to pick the fluffy bolls.

FLOWERS AND BOLLS

Cotton plants grow quickly and soon produce white flowers. When the bolls are ripe, they split open to reveal fluffy white cotton. This is when harvesting must start.

HARVESTING
Cotton was once picked by hand, but machines now do the job much more quickly. The cotton is picked and then the fluffy bolls go into big trailers and are taken to the cotton gins.

LINT
After harvesting, the cotton bolls are taken to the cotton gin, where the cotton fibers, called lint, are separated from the seeds and the husks. The lint is then pressed into large bales, as shown here, before it is spun into thread.

LOOMS
When the cotton has been spun into thread or yarn, it can be woven into a wide range of fabrics, from sheets and curtains to handkerchieves and bandages. Here, the cotton is being woven into a long roll of curtain material on a large loom.

cottonseed has a short fuzz called linters. Linters are used in making plastics, explosives, medical cotton, and stuffing for cushions.

Cotton farmers lose about 20 percent of their crop to pests and disease. Boll weevils account for 90 percent of the damage by pests. Other pests include bollworms, aphids, and thrips (see APHID; BOLL WEEVIL; BOLLWORM; THRIP). Many of these insects have developed a resistance to the insecticides usually sprayed on the bolls, forcing farmers to try other means of insect control. In addition, microscopic worms called nematodes may attack cotton plant roots and expose them to disease. Most of these diseases, such as blight, are caused by fungi. Farmers use various fungicides to try to control the diseases (see FUNGUS; NEMATODE). Scientists are experimenting with selective breeding techniques in an attempt to develop plants with greater resistance to pests and disease.
See also BREEDING.

COTTONMOUTH The cottonmouth is a poisonous snake that belongs to the pit viper family. The snake is called a cottonmouth because the inside of its mouth is white. The cottonmouth is sometimes called a water moccasin. It can grow to lengths of 60 in. [150 cm] but is usually somewhat smaller. Cottonmouths are dark brown above and lighter below, with dark bands across their bodies. They closely resemble nonpoisonous water snakes. Cottonmouths are found in the southern and central United States. They live in swamps and along rivers, where they eat fish, reptiles, and small mammals. They are dangerous to humans.

COTYLEDON (kŏt′l ēd′n) The cotyledon is a part of the embryo plant, which is the undeveloped plant still wrapped up in the seed (see EMBRYO). The cotyledon is also called a seed leaf. In many young plants, it is the first leaf to appear above the ground. The seeds of pines and other conifers may contain more than 20 cotyledons. Flowering plants are divided into two major groups according to the number of cotyledons in their seeds. The dicotyledons, which include beans and cabbages, have two cotyledons. The monocotyledons have only one. Monocotyledons include corn and all other grasses, and most other plants with long, narrow leaves (see

COTYLEDON
This seedling clearly shows the two seed leaves or cotyledons characteristic of the dicotyledon group of flowering plants. The young shoot carrying the first true leaves is growing up between the cotyledons, which will wither when the true leaves open and start to make food.

DICOTYLEDON; MONOCOTYLEDON). In some seeds, including peas and beans, the cotyledons are thick and fleshy, and they are packed with stored food. In many other seeds, the cotyledons are thin and much more leaflike. The food is stored around them in a tissue called endosperm (see ENDOSPERM).

When seeds start to grow, the cotyledons may stay underground, as with peas and broad beans, or they may grow aboveground, as with French beans and cabbages (see GERMINATION). Cotyledons appearing aboveground may turn green and start to make food by photosynthesis, but they do not last very long. They die as soon as the true leaves open and start to make food (see PHOTOSYNTHESIS). *See also* PLANT KINGDOM.   **PROJECT 72**

COULOMB (kōō′lŏm′) A coulomb is a unit of electricity. One coulomb is the electric charge that flows past a point in an electrical circuit in one second when the current is one ampere. Ampere is the unit that measures the strength of a current or the rate at which charge flows. A coulomb is equal to the charge on about 6 quintillion (6 x 10^{18}) electrons. Electrons are fundamental "particles of electricity." The coulomb was named in honor of Charles de Coulomb, a French physicist.
See also AMPERE; COULOMB, CHARLES DE; CURRENT, ELECTRIC.

COULOMB, CHARLES DE (1736–1806) Charles de Coulomb was a French scientist and inventor who made important contributions to the fields of electricity, magnetism, and friction. He formulated Coulomb's law, which states that the force between two electric charges, or magnetic poles, varies inversely as the square of the distance between them.

Coulomb invented a device called a torsion balance to measure the force of magnetic and electrical attraction. In 1779, he received a prize from the Royal Academy of Sciences for a paper on magnetic needles. Two years later, in 1781, the academy awarded him another prize for a paper titled *Theory of Simple Machines*. The unit of quantity of electric charge, the coulomb, was named in his honor.
See also COULOMB.

COUSTEAU, JACQUES-YVES (1910–)

Jacques-Yves Cousteau is a French oceanographer, motion picture producer, and author. He has developed many techniques for undersea exploration. In 1943, he helped invent the Aqua-Lung, a self-contained breathing device that allows a diver to move about freely underwater for long periods of time. Cousteau also built the first underwater diving station and an underwater observation vehicle called the *Soucoupe Plongeante* (diving saucer).

Starting in 1951, Cousteau explored the world's oceans in his research ship *Calypso*. He invented a process for using a camera underwater and used this technique to film the popular television series *The Undersea World of Jacques Cousteau*.

Cousteau wrote books on sea life that have been translated into several languages. These books include: *The Silent World* (1953), *The Living Sea* (1963), and *World Without Sun* (1964). Cousteau has been active in marine conservation. He has spoken out often about the killing of whales and seals. In 1960, he and Prince Rainier III of Monaco protested against France's plan to dump radioactive wastes into the Mediterranean Sea. French officials abandoned the plan soon after the protest.
See also OCEANOGRAPHY.

COWBIRD

A cowbird is a bird that belongs to the blackbird family, Icteridae. It is about 7 in. [17.5 cm] long. Cowbirds were named for their habit of following grazing cows in the pasture and eating the insects that the cows stir up from the grass. There are two species of cowbirds in North America. The bronzed cowbird is found only in parts of the southwestern United States and Mexico. It is dark brown with black wings. The brown-headed cowbird is found throughout the United States, Canada, and Mexico. Males have a black body with a brown head. Females are dull brown. Cowbirds are known for their practice of laying eggs in the nests of other birds. The cowbird never returns to the nest. The bird that built the nest hatches and raises the young cowbird with the other hatchlings of the nest.
See also BLACKBIRD; PARASITE.

COWRIE

A cowrie is a sea snail whose egg-shaped shell has a long, narrow slit on the underside. There are over 150 different kinds of cowries, ranging in length from about 0.5 to 6.0 in. [1.3 to 15 cm]. They are all carnivorous (meat-eating) creatures feeding on corals, sea anemones, and sponges. Nearly all of them live in shallow, coastal waters of warm seas. The shells of many species are brightly colored, and so smooth that they look like china. Some kinds of cowries are very rare and their shells are worth hundreds of dollars to collectors. Cowrie shells were once used as money in China, Africa, and India.
See also SHELL; SNAIL.

COWRIE
The cowrie is a type of mollusk that lives on the sea bottom. The colorful shiny shells of cowries are valued by collectors.

COYOTE The coyote is a carnivorous mammal belonging to the same family as the dog and the wolf (see CARNIVORE; MAMMAL). Coyotes adapt well to environmental changes and are found in the central and western regions of North America from Alaska through Mexico.

The coyote is 16 to 20 in. [40 to 50 cm] tall at the shoulder and weighs as much as 55 lb. [25 kg]. It has soft, yellowish black fur and a bushy tail. The coyote has very keen senses and feeds mostly on rats, gophers, and other rodents. Because coyotes also attack stray livestock, they are often hunted and trapped by farmers. Coyotes are also called prairie wolves.

COYOTE
The coyote is famous for its howl, which is most often heard at dusk and at dawn. Several coyotes often howl together and the sound is quite spooky as it rings over the countryside.

CPU The CPU (Central Processing Unit) is the part of a computer where instructions are interpreted and carried out. It directs and coordinates operations throughout the whole computer. It consists of two main parts, a control unit and an arithmetic/logic unit (ALU). The control unit controls operations within the computer according to instructions stored in the computer's memory. The instructions are in the form of a binary code (see BINARY NUMBERS). The code contains details of what the computer must do and where the data necessary to carry out operations is stored in the computer's memory. The control unit responds to these instructions by sending commands to the ALU. The ALU receives data from the computer's memory, performs calculations on them, and sends the result back to the memory. The result may also be sent to an output device such as a monitor screen. The movement of data between the memory and the ALU is controlled by the CPU's control unit. The CPU of a personal computer is contained within a single silicon chip, the microprocessor. *See also* COMPUTER.

CRAB A crab is an animal of the crustacean class. Crabs and other crustaceans belong to the phylum Arthropoda (see ARTHROPODA; CRUSTACEAN). The crab's body is covered by a hard shell and has five pairs of jointed legs. Usually, the front pair of legs has strong, pincerlike claws. The crab usually walks sideways. It swims either sideways or backwards. Some crabs live in fresh water, but the great majority of the 4,500 or so species live in the sea. They eat almost anything they can find, including dead animals and other decaying matter.

A single female crab may lay between one million and five million tiny eggs at one time. Crabs hatch from their eggs as tiny larvae that swim freely. They soon undergo bodily changes and enter a second larval stage. During this stage, their adult form slowly develops. Many species molt—that is, shed their shells—weekly or monthly as they grow. Some species increase their size by one-third each time they molt. They stop molting after reaching maturity during their second or third year (see LARVA; MOLTING).

Some crabs live in shallow waters along the shore. Others live in deep waters. For example, the fiddler crab lives in burrows in the banks of salty tidal streams. The male fiddler crab has one claw much larger than the other and waves it about to attract females.

The smallest crabs are the tiny pea crabs, or oyster crabs, whose shells are only 1/4 in. [6 mm] across. The female pea crab lives in the shells of live oysters.

The hermit crab sticks the hind end of its body, which is soft and unprotected, into an empty snail shell and drags it around wherever it goes. As the crab grows, it changes the shell from time to time for a larger one.

The blue crab is the most common crab sold as food in markets of the eastern United States. When

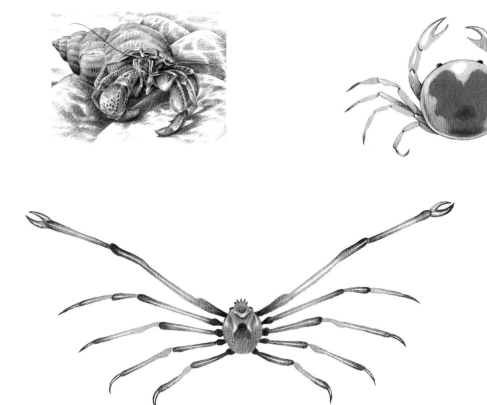

CRAB

The hermit crab (top left) commonly uses a whelk shell for its home. The pea crab (top right) has a very smooth shell—otherwise it would irritate the oysters in whose shells it lives. The shell of the giant spider crab (left) from Japan is only 12 in. [30 cm] across, but its outstretched claws often span more than 10 ft. [3 m]. This crab lives in deep water and is sometimes called the "stilt crab."

these crabs have shed their shells, and the new ones have not yet hardened, they are sold as soft-shelled crabs.

The Alaska king crab is caught by American and Japanese fishing crews. As one of the largest crabs, its 12-lb. [5.4-kg] body supplies much meat. Largest of all crabs is the Japanese spider crab. Some of these crabs have been found to have a claw span of 12 ft. [3.6 m].

CRAB NEBULA The Crab Nebula is a huge cloud of glowing gases that lies in the constellation Taurus. It is about 6,500 light-years from Earth (see CONSTELLATION; LIGHT-YEAR).

The Crab Nebula is the result of a violently exploding star, called a supernova. In the year 1054, the Chinese observed a supernova explosion in the constellation Taurus. What remains from that explosion today is the crab-shaped gas cloud called the Crab Nebula.
See also SUPERNOVA.

CRACKING Cracking, or pyrolysis, is the breaking up of chemical substances by heat. Cracking is a common practice in petroleum refining. One method of cracking is called thermal cracking. Thermal cracking is the use of steady heat and pressure to break down heavier hydrocarbons into lighter ones, such as gasoline (see HYDROCARBON). The oil industry first used this process in 1913. Thermal cracking increases the quality and quantity of gasoline obtained from crude oil.

Most cracking in petroleum is done with the help of a catalyst (see CATALYST). Catalytic cracking, also called cat cracking, produces more gasoline of higher quality than thermal cracking. Catalytic cracking was developed in 1928 and came into use in the 1930s. In this process, petroleum engineers pass petroleum vapor over a mixture of alumina and silica, certain kinds of clay, or other catalysts.

Fluid cat cracking is the process most widely used in petroleum refining. Refineries began using this method in 1942. In this process, a powdered catalyst moves through the petroleum as a fluid. Fluid cat cracking is used to produce aviation gasoline, raw materials for synthetic rubber, and other petroleum products. The method is now a standard practice in the chemical industry and many other industries.
See also GASOLINE; PETROLEUM.

CRANE A crane is a tall bird that belongs to the family Gruidae. It has long legs, a long neck, and a long, slender bill. Cranes may grow as tall as 45 in. [112.5 cm] and have a wingspan of 90 in. [225 cm]. They eat insects, frogs, and small rodents. There are about sixteen species of cranes around the world, but only two live in North America. The whooping crane is endangered, with only about 200 birds alive today (see ENDANGERED SPECIES). The bird breeds in Canada in the summer and spends the winter on the coast of Texas. The sandhill crane is more common and can be found over a wide area of North America and also in Siberia. Biologists have studied both types of North American cranes and have learned how to raise them. It now appears that the number of these beautiful birds is again increasing.

CRANE

The whooping crane is one of the world's rarest birds. Crane chicks can walk soon after hatching, but they cannot fly until they are about three months old.

CRANE (MACHINE) A crane is a machine that can lift and move heavy loads. It is used mainly in the construction of buildings and other projects. A crane has a long, movable arm called a boom or a jib. The machine's name comes from its resemblance to the crane bird, which has a long neck.

There are two basic kinds of cranes: those that are fixed and those that are mobile. The mobile cranes are more common. The crawler is a mobile crane mounted on a vehicle with wheels or tractorlike tracks. Crawler cranes can lift loads of up to 72 tons [80 metric tons] and can have boom lengths of 170 ft. [50 m] or more.

Another type of crane familiar to those who live around urban construction is the hammerhead crane, sometimes called the tower crane. It is used in the erection of tall buildings, such as skyscrapers. It has a long horizontal jib that is cantilevered and mounted on a tower (see CANTILEVER). The tower can be raised by jacking it up, floor by floor, as the building becomes taller. The load is suspended from a trolley that moves along the jib.

Other mobile cranes are the creeper cranes used in the construction of steel-arch bridges and the climbing cranes used in the construction of the towers for suspension bridges.

CRANE (MACHINE)

Cranes lift materials up to workers at the top of tall construction projects.

CRANE FLY Crane flies are slender flies with two glassy wings that are often cloudy or spotted. The flies have thin antennae and long, very fragile legs that break off easily (see ANTENNAE). Crane flies have wingspans of 0.25 to 3 in. [6 to 75 mm].

Crane flies live in all kinds of places, but are especially common on grassland. Their larvae live in the soil and are sometimes called leather jackets. The larvae of some species do considerable damage to the roots of grasses and other plants.
See also LARVA.

CRANE FLY

Like all true flies, crane flies have only a single pair of wings. They are common in the fall, when the females lay their eggs in grasses and lawns. The larvae that hatch from the eggs often damage plant roots.

CRAPPIE A crappie is a freshwater fish that belongs to the sunfish family, Centrarchidae (see SUNFISH). The crappie has a deep, flat body with broad fins. It may grow to lengths of 12 in. [30 cm]. There are two species of crappies: the white crappie and the black crappie. They were originally found in central and eastern North America but have been introduced throughout the continent. The black crappie, also called a calico bass in some places, is the more widespread species.

CRATER A crater is a funnel- or cup-shaped hole formed in the surface of a celestial body, such as the earth or moon. For example, the crater Clavius on the moon is about 4 mi. [6.5 km] deep and has a diameter of 146 mi. [235 km]. Some craters on Earth are formed by the impact of meteorites, solid objects from space that hit the earth (see METEOR). For example, Meteor Crater in Arizona is about 600 ft. [183 m] deep and has a diameter of 4,200 ft [1,280 m]. However, most craters on the earth lie at the top of volcanic cones (see VOLCANO). Some volcanic craters are formed as magma (molten

rock) from erupting volcanoes hardens and builds up around the openings of the volcanoes. Other volcanic craters, such as Crater Lake in Oregon and Kilauea in Hawaii, are formed when the top of the volcano sinks because the level of magma underneath has decreased due to volcanic eruptions. These craters are called calderas (see CALDERA).

CRATER

Wizard Island is a small volcanic cone in Oregon's Crater Lake. This cone has its own small crater at its peak.

CRAYFISH A crayfish is a crustacean that belongs to the order Decapoda. It is related to crabs, shrimp, and lobsters (see CRUSTACEAN). The crayfish looks like a small lobster. It has eight legs, two antennae, and two pincerlike claws with which to capture food (see ANTENNAE). A crayfish also has an exoskeleton, which is a hard shell that protects its body. The exoskeleton is made of chitin and calcium salts (see CHITIN; SKELETON). Crayfish may grow as long as 6 in. [15 cm]. They live in freshwater ponds and streams, feeding on plants and small or dead animals. The crayfish is also called a crawdad or crawfish. Some species of crayfish are eaten by people.

CREOSOTE BUSH The creosote (krē′ə sōt′) bush is an evergreen shrub that grows in the deserts of the southwestern United States and Mexico. It reaches a height of 5 to 8.25 ft. [1.5 to 2.5 m]. Its tangled branches have lobed leaves that produce a strong-smelling tarlike resin (see RESIN). The creosote flower is small and yellow, and the inedible fruit is round and white. The roots spread widely under the sand to trap as much of the infrequent rain as possible. Creosote is also called greasewood.

CREOSOTE BUSH

Creosote bushes are often spaced widely over the desert because their roots produce chemicals that prevent other bushes from growing too near to them.

CRETACEOUS PERIOD (krĭ tā′shəs pĭr′ē-əd) The Cretaceous period began about 146 million years ago and lasted about 81 million years. It is the last period of the Mesozoic era, also called the age of dinosaurs. Reptiles were the dominant animals on land and in the sea. At the end of the Cretaceous period, all of the dinosaur type of

CRETACEOUS PERIOD

Corythosaurus was a crested duck-billed dinosaur that lived in North America during the Cretaceous period.

reptiles became extinct. Soon, mammals and birds became the dominant land creatures.

During the Cretaceous period, the climate was fairly mild, though parts of Australia were glaciated (see GLACIATION). Chalk deposits formed in North America and Europe. Many oil deposits, such as those in Texas, are found in Cretaceous rocks.

Angiosperms (flowering plants) evolved during the Cretaceous period. By the end of the period, they were the dominant land plants.

See also DINOSAUR; GEOLOGICAL TIME SCALE.

CRICK, FRANCIS HARRY COMPTON

(1916–) Francis Crick, a British biologist, was originally a physicist. He helped develop radar during World War II. In 1949, he began to do research work in molecular biology at Cambridge University.

Crick became famous as one of the discoverers of the double-helix structure of DNA, the nucleic acid that is the chemical basis of heredity (see DNA). In 1953, Crick and James D. Watson built a model of the DNA molecule. This model showed how the molecule could reproduce itself during cell division. The model, resembling a twisted ladder, is called the Watson-Crick model (see WATSON, JAMES DEWEY).

For their discovery, Crick and Watson shared the 1962 Nobel Prize in physiology or medicine with Maurice Wilkins. Wilkins took the X-ray diffraction photographs of DNA from which Crick and Watson worked.

See also CHROMOSOME; GENETICS.

CRICKET Crickets are jumping insects belonging to the order Orthoptera. They have two taillike feelers at the end of the abdomen. Female crickets have a third taillike structure called an ovipositor. The ovipositor is a long tube used for laying eggs. Although most species have four flat wings, some are wingless. Males are able to make a sound by rubbing their two front wings together. Both sexes have two antennae, which are longer than their bodies (see ANTENNAE).

The most common species in the United States is the field cricket, a blackish brown insect that is about 1 in. [2.5 cm] long. Like all crickets, it has hearing organs on its front legs. Crickets are sometimes considered pests because they can destroy small amounts of cereal crops. In some countries, crickets are caged and kept as singing pets.

See also GRASSHOPPER.

CRICKET

The house cricket eats almost anything, and can be found in and around buildings throughout the world.

CRINOID (krī′noid′) Crinoids are a class of invertebrate sea animals belonging to the phylum Echinodermata (see ECHINODERMATA). There are over seven hundred living species. Some are stalked sea lilies that attach themselves to the bottom of the sea and look more like plants than animals. Others are free-living, stalkless feather stars (see FEATHER STAR).

More than two thousand extinct crinoids have been identified from fossils. Geologists use these fossils to identify the relative ages of rocks. Crinoidal limestone is made up largely of skeletons of sea lilies.

See also FOSSIL.

CRINOID

This is a fossil of the crinoid sea lily called Gissocrinus. It lived on the seabed during the Silurian period, about 400 million years ago.

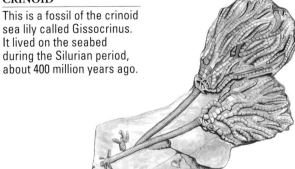

CROCODILE The crocodile is a large reptile with a long body, short legs, and a powerful tail and jaws. Its pointed snout and long, partially exposed sharp teeth, especially the big front tooth on the lower jaw, help distinguish it from its relative, the alligator. When the mouth is closed, this tooth sticks up on the outside of the snout. The crocodile is generally more aggressive than the alligator and may attack large animals such as deer or even human beings (see ALLIGATOR).

Crocodiles live in tropical areas throughout the world, usually in swamps or marshes or along slow-moving rivers. They have partially webbed feet, which help them to swim and to walk on wet or muddy ground. Since the eyes and nostrils are higher than the rest of the head, a crocodile can hide in the water, staying almost completely submerged, and still be able to breathe and see its prey. The crocodile is carnivorous and usually feeds on fish, birds, or small mammals (see CARNIVORE).

The female can lay 50 or more hard-shelled eggs. She places them in a pit in the ground near water. She stays with the eggs for about four months, until they begin to hatch.

Crocodiles once existed in large numbers in many parts of the world. One extinct variety measured 50 ft. [15 m] long and weighed several tons. Of the twelve surviving species, the only native

CROCODILE

Crocodiles cool themselves on hot days by holding their mouths open for long periods and losing heat from the moist lining of the mouth. The big lower tooth fits into the notch near the front of the upper jaw when the jaws are closed.

crocodile in the United States is the American crocodile. It is about 12 ft. [3.7 m] long. The Nile crocodile is about 15 ft. [4.6 m] long and is found throughout Africa. Skin hunters have killed so many of these crocodiles that they are now endangered species and are protected by law in most places.

See also ENDANGERED SPECIES; REPTILE.

CROCUS The crocus is a genus of seventy-five flowering plants of the iris family that are native to the Alps, the Mediterranean area, and western Asia. The crocus grows from a corm and produces cuplike flowers in the spring or fall (see BULB AND CORM). The flowers have six perianth sections, three stamens, and three branched stigmas (see FLOWER). The flowers, which grow near the ground, are mostly white or mauve, but there are many cultivated forms. The flowers close up at night and on overcast days (see MOVEMENT OF PLANTS).

Saffron, a yellow spice used in cooking, is made from the dried stigmas of the saffron crocus from the Mediterranean area and the Middle East.

CROCUS
Crocuses are among the first flowers to bloom in late winter and early spring. The autumn crocus, or saffron crocus, blooms in the fall. It is used to make a spice for coloring and flavoring foods. The crocus is native to the Alps, the area around the Mediterranean Sea, and western Asia.

CRO-MAGNON
Cro-Magnon people were skillful hunters who used shaped animal furs to keep warm. Their organized, tribal society allowed time for activities beyond simple survival, such as painting and carving.

CRO-MAGNON Cro-Magnons are the oldest known representatives of the human race, or *Homo sapiens* (see HUMAN BEING). They lived from about 37,000 to 10,000 years ago throughout Europe and parts of Asia and northern Africa. The existence of Cro-Magnon people was discovered in 1868 when the first skeletons were found in the Cro-Magnon cave in southwestern France. Since then, more than one hundred skeletons and parts of skeletons have been found.

Cro-Magnons first appeared just after the coldest stage of the last ice age. They followed the Neanderthals, though the relationship between the two groups is not clear. Cro-Magnons had large brains and were tall and muscular. The average height of a Cro-Magnon was about 5.7 ft. [173 cm], though at least one skeleton, that of the "Old Man of Cro-Magnon," was about 6.3 ft. [190 cm] tall. Bone structure and general appearance were probably almost identical to that of modern human beings.

Cro-Magnons were skillful hunters. They often formed groups to hunt the huge mammoths and woolly rhinoceroses. They probably killed these animals by stampeding them over cliffs or into bogs. Their weapons were made from ivory, bone, and stone. Tools were used to make these weapons and to prepare animal skins for use as clothing and shelter. The quality of these tools greatly improved as time went on. Many of the Cro-Magnon people lived in huts built in the open or under rocky overhangs. Others used caves for shelter.

The earliest existing artwork is that of the Cro-Magnon people. There are various figures sculpted from clay, ivory, and bone. These probably had a role in religious ceremonies. There are also beautiful paintings in some of the caves. Most of the paintings show various stages of hunting. It is thought that these paintings were offerings to the gods to bring good luck to the hunters.

The skeletons show that many Cro-Magnon people suffered from caries (tooth decay) and other disorders. The dead were usually decorated with paint and buried in shallow graves. This indicates that the Cro-Magnons probably believed in an afterlife and were preparing the dead for entry into that afterlife.

CROOKES, SIR WILLIAM (1832–1919)

Sir William Crookes was a British physicist and scientist who discovered the element thallium. He was also noted for his studies of cathode rays.

In 1879, Crookes invented the Crookes tube, a type of electronic vacuum tube that produces cathode rays. Cathode rays are streams of negatively charged electrons. The Crookes tube was the forerunner of the television picture tube (see CATHODE-RAY TUBE). Crookes also invented the radiometer, an instrument that measures light energy, and the spinthariscope, a device for detecting alpha particles (see ALPHA PARTICLE).

Crookes studied selenium compounds and used the principle of spectrum analysis to identify the element thallium. In 1873, after several years of investigation, he was able to determine that its atomic weight was 204.37 (see ELEMENT; SPECTRUM).

Crookes was one of the leading authorities of his time on the industrial uses of chemistry. He was also one of the leading investigators of psychic phenomena and spiritualism in the late 1800s and early 1900s.

See also ELECTRONICS; VACUUM TUBE.

CROP

A crop is any plant or animal raised for human use. Examples of crops raised for food include cattle, hogs, fruits, grains, and vegetables. Fiber crops, such as cotton and hemp, are grown to make clothing and textiles. Flowers, lawn grasses, and decorative trees and shrubs are types of ornamental crops.

See also AGRICULTURE.

CROP (ZOOLOGY)

A crop is a space in the upper body of certain animals, such as birds, crustaceans, and insects, where undigested food is stored before being digested. The food moves from the crop to other digestive organs.

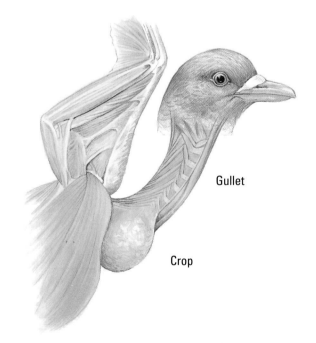

Gullet

Crop

CROP

A bird's crop is a pouch at the bottom end of the gullet. Seeds and other foods are stored in the crop before passing into the stomach for digestion. Some birds use the crop to carry food back to their nestlings. The pigeon's crop even produces a milky fluid that is fed to the nestlings.

CROSSBILL Crossbills are small, colorful birds belonging to the finch family, Fringillidae. As the crossbill's name indicates, the top and bottom of its bill are crossed over each other. The upper part of the bill does not line up with the bottom part. Rather, the upper part curves to one side. This crossing arrangement makes it easier for the bird to pull seeds out of the pine cones and spruce cones upon which it feeds.

There are four species of crossbills. Two of them, the red crossbill and the white-winged crossbill, live in North America.

See also ADAPTATION; FINCH.

CROSSBILL

Crossbills get their name from the crossed beak that they use to pry open the cones of pine and spruce to get at the seeds on which they feed.

CROW Crows are large, black or black and white birds belonging to the family Corvidae. They are related to the jay, magpie, and raven (see BLUE JAY;

CROW

The pied crow (left) has the heavy beak typical of the crow family. This scavenging bird lives in many parts of Africa and often feeds on animal carcasses. It is common in towns and frequently feeds at garbage dumps.

MAGPIE; RAVEN). Crows may grow to nearly 20 in. [55 cm] long. They have very broad wings. They eat a variety of plants and animals, including the flesh of dead animals. The common crow is found throughout North America. Its call is the familiar "caw-caw." The slightly smaller fish crow is found along the Gulf and Atlantic coasts of the United States. The even smaller northwestern crow is found along the Pacific coastline of the state of Washington and north to Canada and Alaska.

CROWFOOT FAMILY The crowfoot family (the Ranunculaceae) includes more than two thousand dicotyledonous herbaceous plants, most of which grow in temperate regions (see HERBACEOUS PLANT; DICOTYLEDON). The family gets its name from the leaves, which are deeply divided and look somewhat like the foot of a bird. The flowers usually consist of five petals and five sepals (petallike structures that are usually green), though the number may vary from two to fifteen. In some species, the petals are missing, and the sepals are brightly colored. There are usually many stamens and carpels arranged in a spiral inside the perianth. The family includes the buttercups as well as the crowfoots.

See also FLOWER.

CROWFOOT FAMILY

Water crowfoots grow in or near water. There are several species, all with white flowers. They usually have normal leaves floating on the water surface and hairlike leaves under the water. Crowfoots growing in fast-flowing streams generally have only the submerged, hairlike leaves.

CRUSTACEAN The crustaceans are a class of some thirty thousand arthropods. They are invertebrates with hard outer coverings called exoskeletons (see ARTHROPODA; INVERTEBRATE; SKELETON). An exoskeleton may be thin and semitransparent, or it may be heavy and bonelike. Since the exoskeleton is made mainly of chitin, its hardness depends on the amount of lime present with the chitin (see CHITIN). Many crustaceans have a carapace, a rigid, protective shield covering most of the head and body. All crustaceans have jointed legs or modified legs on each body segment. Some of these legs are used for walking or swimming; others are modified as claws, pincers, or mouth parts, and in females some are used to hold the eggs. Crustaceans are different from all other arthropods because they have two pairs of antennae instead of one (see ANTENNAE). Many larger crustaceans, such as the lobster, have compound eyes on movable stalks (see EYE AND VISION).

Crustaceans vary in size from tiny water fleas at 0.01 in. [0.25 mm] long to a species of crab with a leg span of about 12 ft. [3.5 m]. Although most crustaceans live in the water and breathe through gills, some species, such as the wood louse, live on land, although they are still confined to damp places. Crustaceans usually reproduce by laying eggs that hatch in the water. Since the exoskeleton does not change size as the crustacean grows, it must be shed several times in a process called molting. Molting is controlled by hormones released by glands located in the eye stalks and body (see HORMONE; MOLTING).

Crustaceans are an important source of food for human beings, whales, fishes, and many other organisms. Copepods, a group of small crustaceans, are an important part of plankton.
See also PLANKTON.

CRYOGENICS Cryogenics is the branch of physics that deals with the behavior of substances at very low temperatures. It also deals with ways of producing such temperatures and with the uses to which they are put. To be considered cryogenic, a temperature must fall in the range from about -184°F [-120°C] to nearly -459.67°F [-273.15°C], which is absolute zero (see ABSOLUTE ZERO).

Cryogenics is now more than a century old. It was born in 1877 when oxygen was liquefied at its boiling point of -297°F [-183°C]. This breakthrough was achieved simultaneously by the Swiss physicist Rasul Pictet and the French engineer Louis Cailletet. The liquefaction of nitrogen gas soon followed. Much earlier, in 1823, Michael Faraday had laid the groundwork for this new science by showing that all the gases known at that time could be liquefied (see FARADAY, MICHAEL). In 1898, Sir James Dewar liquefied hydrogen. Stubborn helium was finally liquefied in 1908 by the Dutch physicist Heike Kamerlingh-Onnes. This achievement was a milestone in cryogenics. Liquefying helium had produced a temperature much lower than anyone had ever observed before. This opened up a whole new area of research.

Using liquid helium, physicists and engineers all over the world began to study the effect of low

CRUSTACEAN
The spiny lobster lacks the powerful claws of many of its relatives, but defends itself by lashing out with its long, spiny antennae. Its stalked eyes are clearly visible.

temperatures on various materials and processes. In 1911, Kamerlingh-Onnes found that cooling mercury to near absolute zero caused that metal to lose all resistance to electric current. He decided that cooling had changed mercury into a perfect conductor—a superconductor. This was an important discovery. Having no resistance, superconductors can carry large amounts of electricity. Tin, lead, and copper also proved to be superconductors under cryogenic conditions. Research has shown that about two dozen pure metals and many alloys (mixtures of metals) and other compounds are superconductors (see SUPERCONDUCTIVITY).

In 1947, the United States established the first commercial system for liquefying helium. More of this liquid gas became available for research and other uses. Since then cryogenic engineering has passed many milestones in the approach to absolute zero. Temperatures of less than a billionth of a degree above absolute zero have been achieved—too close to distinguish in writing from

CRYOGENICS
Cryogenics is used to preserve blood, sperm, and organs for future use or study.

-459.67°F. It is a law of thermodynamics that absolute zero can only be approached, never reached. This is true because the total absence of heat would mean the total absence of atomic activity in the material, which is not possible. Scientists are now trying to find ways of producing superconductivity at higher temperatures. If they can do this, practical applications will be easier to manage.

Magnets that are superconductive are used for some high-speed vehicles called magnetic levitation vehicles, or maglevs. Maglevs can be held above tracklike guideways by these magnets (see MAGNETIC LEVITATION VEHICLE). Superconducting magnets are also used to bend the paths of atomic particles in particle accelerators (see ACCELERATORS, PARTICLE).

Cryogenics also has made contributions to aerospace technology (see AEROSPACE). Oxygen for astronauts and pilots who fly at high altitudes is stored as a liquid. Cryogenic generators that supply this oxygen take up less room and are lighter than the air tanks and compressors previously used. The fuels that launch spacecraft are made up of hydrogen and oxygen that have been made into liquids by cryogenics. Scientists are researching ways to use liquid hydrogen fuels for such vehicles as automobiles and airplanes. Liquid hydrogen is more efficient and releases less pollutants than fuels used today, such as gasoline. However, liquid hydrogen is still very expensive.

Cryogenics has also been used in food processing to quick-freeze foods (see FOOD PROCESSING). Cryogenics is used in medicine to preserve human blood, sperm, and organs. A cryogenic scalpel (surgical knife) has a freezing tip that performs bloodless surgery. These scalpels are used in eye surgery. They are also used to relieve the tremors of patients with Parkinson's disease by killing the nerve cells that cause the tremors.

CRYOLITE Cryolite ($NaAlF_6$) is a soft mineral that consists of sodium, aluminum, and fluorine. It is usually white but sometimes has a red, brown, or blue tint. Cryolite is also called Greenland spar, because the main source of cryolite is Greenland.

Melted cryolite is used in the process by which

aluminum is produced from bauxite ore. Cryolite is also used in making sodium salts and ceramics, such as porcelain.

CRYSTAL A crystal is a solid with a definite geometric shape (see GEOMETRY). Most nonliving substances, such as salt and sugar, can grow into definite shapes. The shapes consist of smooth, flat surfaces that meet in sharp edges and corners. The process by which such substances grow into these shapes is called crystallization. Substances that do not form crystalline solids are called amorphous solids. Examples of amorphous solids are wax, rubber, and glass. The atoms in amorphous solids have not built up into a definite shape or pattern.

People use crystals such as salt (crystalline sodium chloride) and sugar (crystalline sucrose) to flavor food. Such crystals do not appear to have a definite shape. This is because many substances consist of tiny crystals grouped together in a shapeless bunch. Also, the corners of crystals may be broken so that the basic shape cannot be seen.

How crystals grow By doing a simple experiment, a person can see how crystals form. The first step is to dissolve some table salt in a glass of water. There should be enough salt in the solution so that some of the salt does not dissolve even after a great deal of stirring. The solution should then be poured into a second glass.

The next step is to lay a stick across the top of the second glass. Let a piece of string hang from the stick into the solution. After a month or so, small cube-shaped crystals will have become attached to the string. A similar experiment can be done with potassium aluminum sulfate, which can be bought at a drug store. Potassium aluminum sulfate produces crystals that look like two pyramids joined at the base.

Crystals owe their shapes to the ways in which their atoms are put together. The surfaces of a crystal are flat and smooth because the atoms are arranged in a definite pattern in layers upon layers throughout the crystal. The pattern on which layers of atoms attach themselves to the crystal is called a lattice. The atoms, of course, are too small

CRYSTAL—Quartz
These quartz crystals are made of the elements silicon and oxygen. Different minerals have differently shaped crystals.

to see. However, when X rays or electron beams are passed through a crystal, the rays or beams show the pattern of the atoms by the way they (the rays or beams) come out on the other side of the crystal. Scientists also use special kinds of microscope to study the atoms that form the surface of certain crystals.

Some minerals occur as masses of irregular crystal grains. These crystal grains, described as being anhedral, are not shaped like crystals. They do not have flat surfaces. This is because the grains touched other grains as they grew, instead of growing in a surrounding fluid.

Crystal systems Crystals are grouped into various types by the geometry of the flat surfaces that give them their shapes. The crystal groups also depend on the angles at which the adjoining flat surfaces meet. There are six main types of crystal systems. They are described by their axes, which are imaginary lines through the basic crystal unit. The axes join the flat surfaces that are opposite to and usually parallel with each other.

The isometric system, also called the cubic system, has a cube as its simplest form. Isometric crystals have three axes of equal length, all at right angles to each other. Gold and sodium chloride (table salt) form in such crystals. In the tetragonal system, the simplest form is a prism in which the sides are rectangles, and the top and bottom are squares. Tetragonal crystals have three axes at right angles. One of the axes is shorter than the other two, which are equal. Such minerals as cassiterite and rutile crystallize in the tetragonal system. In the

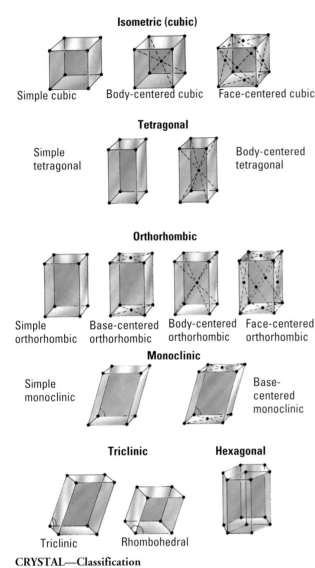

Isometric (cubic)

Simple cubic Body-centered cubic Face-centered cubic

Tetragonal

Simple tetragonal Body-centered tetragonal

Orthorhombic

Simple orthorhombic Base-centered orthorhombic Body-centered orthorhombic Face-centered orthorhombic

Monoclinic

Simple monoclinic Base-centered monoclinic

Triclinic **Hexagonal**

Triclinic Rhombohedral

CRYSTAL—Classification

Crystals are classified into systems by how symmetrical they are. Crystals of the cubic system are symmetrical from almost any angle, but triclinic crystals are not symmetrical at all.

orthorhombic system, the crystals also have three axes at right angles, but the axes are all of different lengths. Topaz has such crystals. The monoclinic system has three axes, all of different lengths. Two of these axes are not at right angles to each other. The monoclinic system is one of the most common. Borax crystallizes in this system. The triclinic system has three unequal axes. None of these axes are at right angles. Only a few crystals, such as rhondonite, crystallize in the triclinic system. In the hexagonal system, a crystal consists of six sides, instead of four as in the other systems. Such crystals have four axes, not three. Three of the four axes are equal in length and are at 60° angles to each other. The fourth axis is longer or shorter and at

right angles to the other three axes. Hexagonal crystals have the basic shape of six-sided prisms. The system includes beryl and calcite crystals. Calcite is an example of a rhombohedral crystal. Rhombohedrals are a subdivision of the triclinic system, though some experts consider them a seventh system. Examples of the six crystal systems are shown in the diagram.

Uses of crystals Crystals have several uses, especially in electricity. Piezoelectric crystals produce an electric signal when their shape is altered by pressure, and again when they return to their original shape (see PIEZOELECTRIC EFFECT). Quartz crystals are used in some hearing aids and microphones to produce electric signals in response to sound waves. Quartz crystals are also used in clocks and watches, and in filters and oscillators for electronic equipment.

See also CLOCK AND WATCH; MICROPHONE; OSCILLATOR; QUARTZ. PROJECT 8

CUCKOO The cuckoos are large birds that belong to the family Cuculidae. They are found throughout most of the world. Five species are found in North America. Perhaps the best-known

CUCKOO

A female cuckoo (top) removes an egg from her host's nest and lays one of her own eggs in its place. The young cuckoo (middle) pushes the other eggs out of the nest, and then gets all the food brought by its foster parents. The young cuckoo (bottom) is much bigger than its foster parents—in this case a winter wren—but they still feed it.

North American cuckoo is the roadrunner (see ROADRUNNER). Cuckoos are slender birds with long tails and long, thin bills. They eat insects, especially caterpillars.

The Eurasian cuckoo, found in Europe, Asia, and Africa, is well known for its unusual egg-laying habits. The female cuckoo does not build its own nest but lays its eggs in the nests of other birds. The eggs look like the eggs of the other birds. The mother cuckoo never returns. The eggs are hatched with the other eggs in the nest. However, the baby cuckoo pushes the other birds out of the nest. The "adopted mother" and usually her mate continue to feed the young cuckoo. Because of this habit, cuckoos are called social parasites (see PARASITE).

CUCUMBER The cucumber is an annual plant belonging to the gourd family (see ANNUAL PLANT; GOURD FAMILY). It has a long, trailing, hairy stem that climbs by means of its tendrils (see TENDRIL). The leaves are triangular, and the bell-shaped yellow or white flowers grow on short stems. Each cucumber plant produces a hundred or more edible fruits, which develop from female flowers. The cucumber fruit varies in length from 1 to 36 in. [2.5 to 90 cm] and has a thin green skin. The fruit itself is usually white or light yellow with many seeds. Although it has little food value, it contains a lot of vitamins. The young cucumber fruit can be eaten raw, as in salads, or can be preserved and eaten as pickles. The mature fruit is hard and usually needs to be cooked before being eaten.

CURIE The curie is a unit used to measure radioactivity. A radioactive material with a strength of one curie produces 3.7×10^{10} nuclear disintegrations a second. A millicurie is a thousandth of a curie. One curie is a strong and harmful amount of radiation (see RADIOACTIVITY).

Originally, a curie was defined as the amount of radioactivity given off by 1 gram of radium (see RADIUM). In other words, radium is such a strong source of radiation that 1 gram of the metal has a strength of one curie. In comparison, nearly 3 million grams of uranium are needed to produce one curie of radiation (see URANIUM).

In many places today, the curie has been replaced by the Système Internationale unit of 1 nuclear disintegration per second.

See also CURIE FAMILY.

CURIE FAMILY Curie is the family name of three famous French physicists. The Curies received three Nobel Prizes for their work concerning radioactivity (see RADIOACTIVITY).

Pierre Curie (1859–1906) Pierre Curie was born in Paris and was the son of a physician. Later he was a professor at the Sorbonne, a university in Paris. In 1880, with his brother Jacques, Pierre Curie discovered that certain crystals, when twisted or vibrated, produce electricity (see PIEZOELECTRIC EFFECT). While still in his twenties, Pierre Curie did important research on the magnetic properties of metals. He found that magnetic substances lose their magnetism when they are heated to a certain temperature. This temperature is called the Curie point.

Marie Curie (1867–1934) Marie Curie was born in Warsaw, Poland, and was the daughter of teachers. Her maiden name was Marie Sklodowska. In 1891, she came to Paris to study physics and chemistry. Four years later, she married Pierre

CURIE FAMILY
Pierre and Marie Curie are shown in their laboratory. The Curies gained worldwide fame for their discovery of two new elements, polonium and radium. They investigated the radioactive properties of the new elements.

Curie. The Curies became interested in radiation given off by radioactive substances.

Marie Curie gave the name *radioactivity* to the powerful radiation that Antoine Becquerel had discovered in uranium ores (see BECQUEREL, ANTOINE HENRI). Marie Curie showed that the strength of radioactivity varied with the amount of uranium. In 1898, she discovered that thorium is a radioactive element. She then found that some minerals are more radioactive than could be accounted for by their thorium or uranium content. She decided that they must contain an unknown but highly radioactive element. Later in the same year, Pierre and Marie Curie discovered two new elements in pitchblende (an important ore of uranium), namely polonium and radium. The amount of radium was only a slight trace. The Curies then set about obtaining a pure radium salt from several tons of pitchblende. They achieved this in 1902. For this work, they received, along with Becquerel, the Nobel Prize for physics in 1903.

In 1911, Marie Curie was awarded the Nobel Prize for chemistry for her work on the isolation of radium and polonium, and for her study of the elements' chemical properties. She later did similar work with her daughter, Irène.

The unit of radioactivity measurement known as the curie was named after Marie Curie (see CURIE). She also played a major role in establishing the Curie Institute of Radium in Paris. Marie Curie died in 1934 of leukemia from the radiation she received during her lifetime. Pierre had died earlier in a street accident.

Irène Joliot-Curie (1897–1956)

Irène Joliot-Curie was the daughter of Marie and Pierre Curie and worked as her mother's assistant in the laboratory at the Institute of Radium. In 1926, she married Frédéric Joliot, and the couple changed their name to Joliot-Curie. They were interested in the atom and bombarded various elements with alpha rays (see ALPHA PARTICLE). In this way, they showed that bombardment of boron produced a radioactive isotope of nitrogen. It was the first radioactive isotope to be produced artificially (see ISOTOPE). This discovery led the way to the production of artificial radioactive elements. In 1935, Frédéric and Irène Joliot-Curie were awarded the Nobel Prize for chemistry.

CURLEW

A curlew is a bird of marshland, prairies, and seashores. It belongs to the sandpiper family, Scolopacidae. It has a long, slender, curved bill and thin, long legs. The curlew's brown body is between 11 and 21 in. [27 and 53 cm] long. Curlews on migration are found in flocks along the Pacific and Gulf coasts of North America. They wade into the water and feed on invertebrates (see INVERTEBRATE). There are four North American species: the long-billed curlew, the whimbrel, the bristle-thighed curlew, and the Eskimo curlew. Although the whimbrel and long-billed curlew are common, the other two birds are rare. The Eskimo curlew is nearly extinct.
See also EXTINCTION.

CURLEW
The western curlew pictured lives in Europe and Asia and is very similar to the long-billed curlew. The beak is ideal for finding food buried in mud or sand.

CURRANT

The currant is a small, bushy shrub belonging to the gooseberry family. It grows wild in cool, moist areas of North America and Europe, and is cultivated for its fruits. The plant produces small, round berries that are used in jams, jellies, wines, and desserts. Red currants, black currants, and golden currants are the most popular species.

CURRANT
The bright red berries of the red currant are pictured here.

CURRENT, ELECTRIC

Electric current is the movement, or flow, of electric charges. When a person switches on a flashlight, the current flows from the batteries, through the switch and the bulb, back to the batteries. The current is measured in amperes. One ampere is equal to a rate of flow of 6.28 x 10^{18} electrons per second, or one coulomb of electricity per second (see AMPERE; COULOMB).

There are two kinds of electric current, alternating current (AC) and direct current (DC). Alternating current is so called because its direction of flow alternates. It builds up to a maximum flow in one direction, decreases to zero, then builds up to a maximum flow in the other direction. This cycle occurs sixty times a second in alternating current used in the United States. Thus, alternating current in the United States is said to have a frequency of sixty hertz (see HERTZ). Other countries have adopted different frequencies.

Alternating current is the most widely used current in the United States because it can easily be increased or decreased in voltage by a transformer, whereas direct current cannot. This enables the user to have alternating current at a convenient and safe voltage regardless of the voltage in the power lines. As a result, the power company can transmit electricity at very high voltages, which is more efficient (see TRANSFORMER; VOLT).

Direct current is electric current that flows in one direction only. It is produced by batteries and direct current generators (see BATTERY; GENERATOR, ELECTRICAL). Electronic equipment, radios, and amplifiers that require direct current can be operated with an alternating current source by using rectifiers. Rectifiers are devices that change alternating current into direct current. Devices that convert direct current into alternating current are called converters or inverters. They allow the operation of AC appliances from DC power sources.

The electricity in flashlights and electric toys is direct current electricity. Metal refining industries are heavy users of direct current electricity. For example, the process for refining aluminum requires large amounts of direct current. Direct current electric motors are sometimes used where good variable speed control is desired, as in cranes, hoists, and elevators.

See also ALTERNATING CURRENT; DIRECT CURRENT; ELECTRICITY; ELECTRIC MOTOR.

PROJECT 29, 30, 31, 37

MOVEMENT OF ELECTRONS

The diagram shows the random movement of electrons in a metal (1), and the organized flow of electrons in a conductor passing direct current (2) and alternating current (3).

1. Conductor passing no current

Electrons flow in all directions

Movements of electrons in a metal conductor not connected to any source of electricity.

2. Conductor passing direct current

Electrons flow from pole to pole

Movements of electrons in a metal conductor connected to the poles of a source of direct current (DC) electricity, such as a battery.

3. Conductor passing alternating current

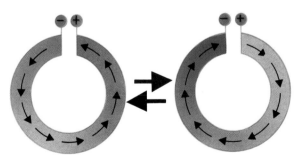

Electrons flow first in one direction

Electrons then flow in reverse direction

Movements of electrons in a metal conductor connected to a source of alternating current (AC) electricity.

CURVE A curve is a line that has no straight part. Many curves have specific mathematical forms and names. These curves might be found in nature. A mathematician might draw a curve on a graph using equations (see ALGEBRA). One group of curves can be found by cutting through different parts of a cone. The diagrams below show how an ellipse, parabola, and hyperbola are obtained from sections of cones. The ellipse is also the path traced out by the planets as they orbit the sun. The path of a shell fired from a gun is a parabola. All of the curves shown, and many other curves as well, can be written as mathematical equations.

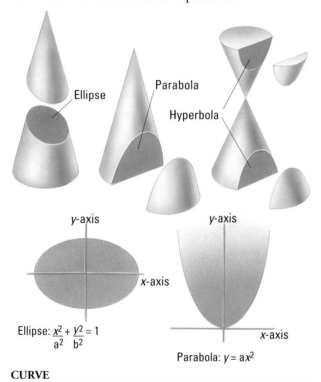

Ellipse: $\dfrac{x^2}{a^2} + \dfrac{y^2}{b^2} = 1$

Parabola: $y = ax^2$

CURVE

An ellipse, parabola, and hyperbola are produced by cutting through cones. The lower set of diagrams shows the curve with the equations that define them, and axes.

CUTICLE The term *cuticle* has a number of meanings, but it is most often used to mean the outer covering of a plant or an animal, especially an arthropod (see ARTHROPOD). In plants, apart from those living in water, the cuticle is a layer of waxy material covering the leaves and stems. It prevents the plants from losing too much water. Among insects and other arthropods the cuticle is a very tough layer secreted by the epidermis, which is the outermost layer of the skin. It is composed largely of a flexible or elastic material called chitin, but in crabs and other crustaceans the chitin is mixed with lime and the cuticle becomes very hard. The outermost layer of human skin is sometimes called the cuticle, especially where it is quite thick—at the base of fingernails and toenails, for example. *See also* SKIN.

CUTTLEFISH (kŭt′l fĭsh′) A cuttlefish is a soft, boneless animal that belongs to the class Cephalopoda (see CEPHALOPOD). The cuttlefish is found in most seas except the seas surrounding the Americas. Most of the animals live in coastal waters. The cuttlefish has a brown body with bands across it and purple spots. It is bright and metallic-looking in the sunlight and often changes color to match various backgrounds (see CAMOUFLAGE). The cuttlefish's oval body is surrounded with a wavy fin. The various species of cuttlefish vary in length from about 3 in. [8 cm] to almost 6 ft. [1.8 m], including the tentacles.

The cuttlefish's shield-shaped body is surrounded by a thick, muscular cloak of skin called the mantle, and it is supported by a light, chalky internal shell called a cuttlebone. The animal can swim slowly by waving the fin that surrounds the mantle. It can also move rapidly backward by forcing water out of the space between the mantle and the body.

The cuttlefish has eight short arms around its mouth, and two long tentacles that shoot out to capture fish and other animals. All carry strong suckers. The arms are used to cling to rocks and to hold the prey while the cuttlefish eats it.

To hide from enemies, the cuttlefish can darken the water as it moves by pouring out an inky substance containing a brown pigment, or coloring matter, called sepia. The sepia used by artists was once made from the substance in the ink sac of the cuttlefish. Because of its lime salts, the cuttlebone is fed to canaries and parrots.

CUTTLEFISH

The cuttlefish can change color very quickly.

CYANIDE (sī′ə nīd′) Cyanides are chemical compounds of nitrogen and carbon with various other elements. Carbon and nitrogen form an incomplete compound called the cyanide radical, represented as –C≡N. The line at left shows where the rest of the molecule or other elements may join (see COMPOUND; RADICAL).

Cyanides are very poisonous. Potassium cyanide (KCN) is used to extract gold and silver from their ores.

CYBERNETICS (sī′bər nĕt′ĭks) Cybernetics is the study of control and communication in both animals (especially humans) and machines. People in the field of cybernetics are especially concerned with information feedback systems, the storage and manipulation of information that guides those systems, and processes for filtering out errors and unrelated messages.

Cybernetics is derived from a Greek word that means "steersman" and refers to the steering of ships. The field of control and communication theory received its name when American mathematician Norbert Wiener published the book *Cybernetics* in 1948. Wiener and his associates thought that the steering engines of a ship were one of the earliest and best-developed forms of a control system that required information feedback mechanisms. Feedback involves the circling back of information to a control device to adjust behavior. For example, if a person exercises strenuously and his or her body builds up heat, information concerning this is fed back to the brain. The brain then signals the body to sweat in order to cool itself. Similarly, if a rocket moves slightly off course, information concerning this error is fed back to a computer, which instructs the rocket to steer back on course.

The role of information feedback is important for communications engineers and the designers of automatic control systems. It is also important for physiologists, psychologists, and sociologists, who study the behavior of animals and human beings.

Bionics is a term that relates to cybernetics. Bionics (*bio*logy + electro*nics*) is the study of how people and other animals perform certain tasks and solve certain problems. This information is applied to the design of computers and other electronic equipment used in control systems.

CYCAD The cycads make up a family of about 100 palmlike gymnosperms (see GYMNOSPERM). These trees are the most primitive seed plants, with fossils proving that they existed during the Mesozoic era, some 65 to 225 million years ago. Most cycads are short and stout, although some reach heights of about 60 ft. [18 m]. The stems are normally unbranched. The large, leathery leaves grow in a rosette (circle) at the top of the stem. In the middle of the rosette is a large, seed-filled cone called a strobilus. The strobilus may weigh as much as 66 lb. [30 kg]. When the seeds mature, part of the strobilus decays and allows the seeds to escape. Some species of cycads live to be more than a thousand years old.

See also CONIFER.

CYCAD

There have been cycads on the earth for over 200 million years, making them among the world's oldest species of plants.

CYCLAMEN

Cultivated cyclamens like this one are much larger than wild cyclamens, which are also called sowbreads.

CYCLAMEN Cyclamen is a genus of sixteen small, herbaceous plants belonging to the primrose family (see HERBACEOUS PLANT; PRIMROSE FAMILY). Native to the Mediterranean region of Europe and western Asia, cyclamens are now grown throughout the world in greenhouses, homes, and gardens. The cyclamen seed grows into a corm (see BULB AND CORM). The leaves produced from this corm often have silver veins. The flowers from the corm are white, rose, or purple and have petals that are bent backward as though they were inside out.

CYCLE Many chemical reactions and physical changes go in cycles. That is, they go from one event through a series of other events until the first event occurs again. Cycles are common in nature. For example, the element nitrogen goes through a cycle of chemical reactions. It is present in the air, then in compounds (combinations of elements) in the soil, then in compounds in living things, then back in the air to start the cycle again (see NITROGEN CYCLE). Similar cycles occur in the body to store and produce energy. Some engines work by repeating a cycle of physical changes.

A cycle is also a complete vibration of a system. For example, a pendulum completes one cycle every time it swings once in one direction and once in the other. In a similar way, alternating current goes from a maximum value in one direction to a

CYCLE

A pendulum is perhaps the most common example of a cycle, and the easiest to understand. After observing a large pendulum, Galileo was inspired to draw up equations defining the orbits of the planets around the sun (see GALILEO).

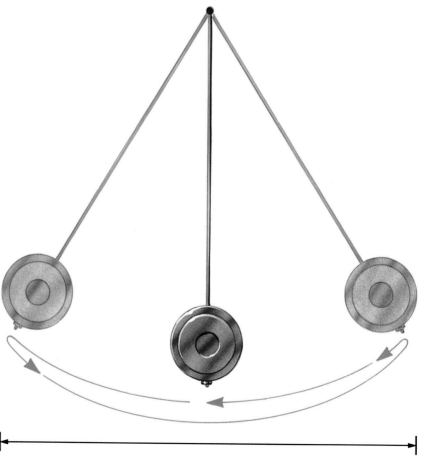

CYCLONE

This bird's-eye-view photograph of a cyclone north of Hawaii was taken during the Apollo 9 moon mission.

maximum value in the opposite direction for each completed cycle. The number of cycles that takes place in one second is called the frequency (see FREQUENCY). The frequencies of sound waves, and of light and other radiation, are also measured in cycles per second, abbreviated as cps. However, instead of the term *cycles per second,* the term *hertz* (*Hz*) is used (see HERTZ). *Hertz* and *cycles per second* mean the same thing.

CYCLING OF NUTRIENTS When plants make food by photosynthesis, they use up some of the carbon dioxide gas in the air (see PHOTOSYN-THESIS). If this gas were not replaced, there would eventually be none left and plant life on the earth would end. But the gas is replaced by means of a continuous recycling process. This circulation of carbon is called the carbon cycle (see CARBON CYCLE). There is a similar circulation of nitrogen and other food materials or nutrients. Plant roots absorb simple compounds of nitrogen and build them into proteins, which are passed on to animals when the plants are eaten. When the animals die, bacteria and fungi break down the proteins and convert them back to simple minerals for the plant roots to absorb again (see DECAY).

CYCLONE A cyclone is a region of low atmospheric pressure usually associated with stormy weather (see ATMOSPHERE). The winds of a cyclone spiral into the area of lowest atmospheric pressure, called the storm center. The cyclonic winds move counterclockwise in the Northern Hemisphere and clockwise in the Southern Hemisphere.

The cyclonic winds mix cold and warm air, producing rain or snow. This type of storm, common during the fall and winter, is called a frontal cyclone. Several times a year, violent frontal cyclones move along the east coast of the United States, bringing heavy rain or snow. These storms are popularly called "northeasters" because the winds blow off the sea from the northeast.

A tropical cyclone develops over the warm waters near the equator. A very strong tropical cyclone that develops over the West Indies or the eastern Pacific Ocean is called a hurricane (see HURRICANE). Usually several hurricanes a year cause damage to regions in the United States. A tropical cyclone that develops over the western Pacific Ocean is called a typhoon.

A tornado is a small but violent cyclone that develops in a large thunderstorm. Tornadoes are common in the midwestern and southern United States.
See also ANTICYCLONE; DEPRESSION; TORNADO; WEATHER.

CYCLOTRON A cyclotron is a type of particle accelerator (see ACCELERATORS, PARTICLE). In a cyclotron, subatomic particles are whirled in a spiral path to high speeds. Physicists learn about sub-atomic particles by smashing them into each other to see how they behave. Physicists use high electric

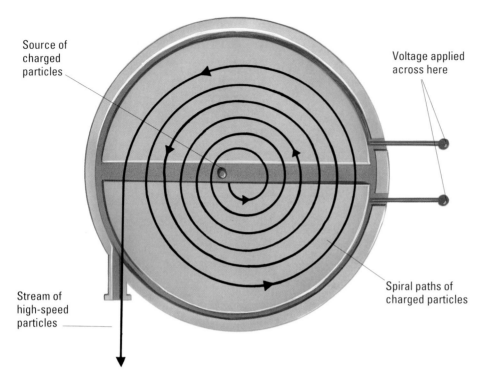

Source of charged particles

Voltage applied across here

Stream of high-speed particles

Spiral paths of charged particles

CYCLOTRON

The cyclotron, an early particle accelerator, consisted of two D-shaped hollow chambers, called dees, enclosed in a vacuum. A voltage was applied across the gap between the dees. Charged particles spiraled outward from the center, picking up energy and accelerating every time they crossed the gap between the dees.

potentials (voltages) to speed up, or accelerate, electrically charged particles such as electrons and protons. In the earliest accelerators, which were built in the 1920s and 1930s, particles were accelerated in straight lines by potentials of up to millions of volts. In the early 1930s, the American physicist Ernest O. Lawrence built the first cyclotron. In this cyclotron, particles were accelerated by a relatively smaller voltage that was applied repeatedly.

The cyclotron consists of two hollow, D-shaped metal chambers called dees. The chambers are kept in a vacuum so that the accelerated particles can move freely without hitting molecules of air (see VACUUM). The two dees are also in a strong magnetic field (see MAGNETIC FIELD). Charged particles are placed into one of the chambers near the center of the cyclotron. At this point they are moving slowly. They move around the dee in a circle because of the magnetic field. They are pulled across the gap into the other dee by a voltage difference between the two, and are slightly speeded up. Because they are moving faster, they revolve in a wider circle in the second dee. Meanwhile, the voltage is reversed, so that when the particles reach the gap again, they are pulled across it in the other direction, with another boost in speed. The particles are boosted many times as they spiral outward, until a beam of the particles,

traveling at nearly the speed of light, flies out of the cyclotron at its outer edge.

Cyclotrons have largely been replaced by more powerful accelerators called synchrotrons.
See also ATOM.

CYPRESS A cypress is an evergreen coniferous tree that belongs to the cypress family, Cupressaceae (see EVERGREEN). The trees grow in North America, Europe, and Asia. Cypresses grow tall and live a very long time. Wood from the cypresses is resistant to rot and is used in the building of houses.

CYPRESS
Cypress twigs are covered with scalelike green leaves. The brown clusters are male cones about to shed their pollen.

CYSTIC FIBROSIS (sĭs'tĭk fĭ brō'səs) Cystic fibrosis is a hereditary disorder, the most common such disorder among white children. There is no cure for cystic fibrosis. About fifty percent of affected children die by age sixteen, though some have lived to age thirty and beyond. Cystic fibrosis affects the exocrine glands, which include the sweat and mucus glands (see GLAND).

The disorder can be detected by testing a child's sweat for abnormal amounts of salt. Those afflicted with the disorder have from two to five times the normal amount of salt in their sweat. Scientists also can perform a test to see if a fetus (unborn baby) has the disorder.

In 1989, scientists were able to locate the defective gene that causes cystic fibrosis. People with relatives who have the disorder can now be tested to see if they also carry the gene (see GENE).

Cystic fibrosis causes the mucus glands to secrete abnormally thick mucus. After discovering the gene that caused cystic fibrosis, scientists learned that people with this defective gene produce an abnormal version of a protein that normally helps keep a balance of salt and water in cells. The abnormal protein allows salt to build up in cells, drawing water away from the mucus linings and making the mucus unusually thick.

The thick mucus clogs glands and ducts (tubes for carrying body fluids) in various organs. For example, the mucus clogs the lungs, making it difficult to breathe (see LUNG). The mucus also collects bacteria, causing infection. Over 90 percent of deaths among people with cystic fibrosis are from lung disease.

Mucus also interferes with the ability of the pancreas to secrete digestive enzymes, which are proteins that cause or speed up certain chemical reactions (see PANCREAS). As a result, foods, especially fats, cannot be completely digested, which leads to malnourishment. The pancreas becomes scarred. This is called fibrosis. Small lumps, called cysts, also form on the pancreas. The name *cystic fibrosis* is derived from these two conditions.

Treatment for the disorder is aimed at making life as normal as possible for the person. Salt supplements, to replace the excessive amount of salt that is secreted, and special digestive enzymes are added to the diet. Treatment also includes antibiotics to fight infection and drugs called expectorants to force the person to cough up excessive mucus (see ANTIBIOTIC). In the more serious stages of the disorder, the lungs may need to be drained daily.

Scientists are researching several new treatments for cystic fibrosis. One type of treatment, called gene therapy, aims to insert a healthy version of the gene that causes cystic fibrosis into a patient's body. The body would then be able to make the normal protein to keep the right amount of salt in cells. If such gene therapy is successful, the patient's body would go on producing the normal protein long after the treatment.

See also GENETICS.

CYTOLOGY Cytology is the study of cells, the basic units of life. A cytologist is a scientist who studies the way cells are organized and how they work. Cytologists have found that every structure in the cell has a special function and that everything an organism does is controlled by the activities of the cells of that organism (see CELL).

Cytology dates back to 1665, when the English scientist Robert Hooke first looked at a piece of cork under a microscope and named the air-filled "boxes" that he saw, *cells*. In 1838, the German biologists Matthias Schleiden and Theodor Schwann proposed the cell theory. The cell theory states that all living things—including all plants and animals—are made of cells. In 1892, the German scientist Oscar Hertwig proposed that all activities of an organism are the result of the activities of the cells of that organism. As a result of this theory, Hertwig was the first to establish cytology as a science.

There are several scientific fields related to cytology. Cytochemistry studies the chemical changes that take place in a cell (see CHEMISTRY). Cytopathology studies diseases of the cell (see PATHOLOGY). Cytogenetics studies the relationship between the activities of the cell and inherited characteristics (see GENETICS; HEREDITY).

See also HOOKE, ROBERT; SCHWANN, THEODOR.

CYTOPLASM Cytoplasm is the portion of a living cell between the nucleus and the cell membrane. It is mostly water and contains enzymes (proteins that cause or speed up chemical reactions) and many structures vital to the life of the cell. These structures are called organelles. The mitochondria produce energy for the cell. Lysosomes contain special enzymes used for digesting food or for helping white blood cells destroy bacteria. The endoplasmic reticulum is a network of canallike passages between the cell membrane and the nucleus. Ribosomes, located along the endoplasmic reticulum, make protein in the cell. Centrioles are active in cell reproduction (see MEIOSIS; MITOSIS). Golgi bodies store and release various substances from the cell. In plant cells, chloroplasts contain chlorophyll and are important in photosynthesis. In most cells, the cytoplasm is always moving in a process called streaming or cyclosis. Cytoplasm consists of two layers: the ectoplasm and the endoplasm.

See also CELL; ECTOPLASM; ENDOPLASM.

D

DAFFODIL The daffodils are about fifty plants belonging to the genus *Narcissus* in the amaryllis family. Daffodils are native to the forests and grasslands of Europe and western Asia. Daffodils are popular garden flowers worldwide because they grow from bulbs and require little care (see BULB AND CORM). The most familiar daffodil is the trumpet narcissus, which has a large flower at the end of each stem. The flower has six petals surrounding the bell-shaped, or trumpetlike, center. Although the flower is usually yellow, there are many cultivated forms, and they include white, red, and orange varieties. The bulb is poisonous if eaten.

See also AMARYLLIS FAMILY; NARCISSUS.

DAFFODIL

These cultivated daffodils clearly show the central trumpet, which encloses the reproductive organs of the flower.

DAGUERREOTYPE (də gâr′ə tīp′) The daguerreotype, also called tintype, was the first permanent photograph. It consisted of a picture reproduced on a thin copper sheet. The daguerreotype was developed in 1839 by the French inventor Louis Daguerre. Daguerre made a polished, silvered copper plate sensitive to light by exposing it to iodine fumes. Then he exposed the plate for three to thirty minutes in a camera. He used mercury vapor to develop the image and fixed, or stopped, the developing process with a solution of sodium thiosulfate. Daguerre improved the process in 1840 by using bromine fumes to sensitize the copper plate and gold chloride solution to enrich the image.

Highlights in a daguerreotype are whitish. Shadows are bare areas that appear dark when the plate is held against a dark background. Daguerreotypes reproduced even the smallest details seen through the camera lens, and they had a long life. Fine-quality daguerreotypes produced in the 1800s can be seen in museums and private collections today. Many people had their portraits taken by this process in the 1800s. Some of the first photographs of the Old West and the Civil War were on daguerreotypes.

See also PHOTOGRAPHY.